My Genes
Made
Me Do It!

by Neil & Briar Whitehead

HUNTINGTON HOUSE PUBLISHERS

Huntington House Publishers
P.O. Box 53788
Lafayette, Louisiana 70505

Library of Congress Card Catalog Number 98-75710
ISBN 1-56384-165-7

Printed in the United States of America

Contents

Acknowledgments

Our thanks to a heterosexual married man, Noel Mosen, who told us in 1987 that he had been a promiscuous gay man for more than twenty years and a gay political activist for more than half that. Our relationship with him started a research project that gave rise to two books: *Craving for Love* (Monarch, UK, 1993) by Briar Whitehead, which examined causes of homosexuality and the process of change from homosexual to heterosexual, and a lengthy political article defending the rights of gays to change their orientation if they wish, which cited abundant scientific evidence of changes in sexual orientation. *My Genes Made Me Do It!* further develops the material in both *Craving for Love* and the article and introduces a lot of new material. Our thanks go to Tony and Jane Collins of Monarch Publications for their assistance, and to a large number of libraries and others that so readily open their holdings to Neil, in the spirit of academic freedom. Also, thanks to Dr. J. Court and Dr. L. R. B. Mann for reading the manuscript and for important suggestions. Finally, thanks to our brothers and sisters in the gay activist community for the huge number of arguments they have produced in favor of the idea that sexual orientation is not changeable. Answering them has been very stimulating.

Dr. Neil Whitehead (Ph.D., biochemistry) has worked for twenty-five years as a research scientist in New Zealand. Briar Whitehead is a journalist and writer. *My Genes Made Me Do It!* is Neil and Briar's third book on the topic of homosexuality.

Introduction

We see and hear it everywhere now: "But aren't gays born that way?" We see it in the psychology and counselling professions, which now widely reflect the view that homosexual people should be counselled toward acceptance of their sexuality.

We see it in the judiciary. For instance, in 1993 the Hawaii Supreme Court decided that it might be unconstitutional to deny marriage licences to homosexuals. For Associate Judge James Burns, the whole matter hung on whether or not homosexuality was "biologically fated."[1] If it's unconstitutional to discriminate on the basis of gender, and gender is biologically fated, then why shouldn't it be unconstitutional to discriminate on the basis of sexual orientation, if homosexuality is also biologically fated? In that case, civil marriage between homosexuals would qualify for constitutional protections.

We see it in political life, in the passage of legislation banning discrimination against homosexuals and granting many benefits approximating those of married couples. If they can't help the way they are, we have no business withholding from homosexuals the rights and privileges allowed other minority groups with immutable characteristics.

We see it in the heads of the church, in merciful men like Archbishop Desmond Tutu, who equates homosexuality with skin color and asks, therefore, why we don't want homosexuals "to give expression to their sexuality in loving acts", since "it is becoming increasingly clear they can do little about [their sexual orientation]." We see it in the debates over ordination of openly practicing homosexuals. "If they can't help the way they are, why should they be denied positions of leadership in the church?" It sounds so even-handed and fair. After all, God in Christ accepts, loves, and includes us all. Compassion is measured against judgmentalism, and Christians know that compassion and mercy are better.

We see it in homosexual people themselves, most of whom want to change their orientation at some stage. More than a third of gays now believe they were born that way—a 400 percent increase in 50 years.[2] They absorb the information that their sexuality is genetic, ingrained, inborn, resistant to change, and their despair and anger fuels the fight for equal freedoms, which can only be ultimately disillusioning because it is based on a powerful untruth.

We see it when the popular press tries to reduce a complex piece of science to a four or five word headline. Usually (in our experience) the press misrepresents science. We're left with a headline like: "Gay gene discovered," or "Genetic basis to homosexuality." Any geneticist worth his salt begins to cry. But most of the rest of us make a mental adjustment of sorts. *"Well, I guess if it's genetic there's not much they can do about it. . . ."*

"Most of the rest of us" include Mr. and Ms. Average Citizen, and the people in the preceding paragraphs— bishops, clergy, laity, members of the judiciary, politicians, psychotherapists, counselors, community leaders. We are usually not scientists. We are busy people who often only have time to scan the headlines, or absorb the first couple of sentences on the TV news such as, "Scientists claim to have found a link between homosexuality and genes." What are we to believe? These, apparently, are the experts speaking. Without the time or special training to check the facts, we capitulate to what seems the fair, decent, compassionate, intelligent thing to do under the circumstances.

We then find we are under pressure to adopt the line that homosexual people are being discriminated against for a sexual orientation they didn't ask to have. Proponents of this line may quote the latest press report linking biology and homosexuality, the sweep of legislation from enlightened legislatures all over the Western world, the official stance of professional organizations, or the shifting position of the church. They may present the moving testimony of a gay person on the receiving end of some ignorant heterosexual "homophobia," and we are left believing that if we are compassionate and informed people (which, of course, we like to think we are) we have no other option.

Not true. So much of what people in the West now believe about homosexuality is not the truth. Misinformed people are quoting other misinformed people so that the blind lead the blind. It suits some people to believe what they do, but many others genuinely don't know what to believe and would welcome the truth if they only knew where to find it.

Here is a very basic truth. There is nothing fixed or final about the homosexual orientation and its natural expression, homosexual behavior. No one has to stay homosexual or lesbian, in orientation or behavior, if he or she doesn't want to and informed support is available. No politician, church leader, church member, judge, counselor, homosexual person, or friend or family of a homosexual person, needs to feel forced into a position on homosexuality based on the apparent immutability of the homosexual orientation. Homosexuality is not inborn, not genetically dictated, not immutable. Nor, for that matter, is heterosexuality or any other human behavior. In fact, our genes do not make us do anything. Whether it's homosexuality, a foul temper, bedwetting, or addiction to chocolate, our genes have very little to do with it.

People who say that homosexuality is fixed and unchangeable don't have a full enough understanding of mainstream genetics. Those who say gays are born that way usually don't know enough about identical twin studies or gene linkage studies, hormonal research, brain structure, medical research into gender, or anthropol-

ogy. They aren't acquainted with the huge amount of
scientific data showing that sexual orientation is extremely
elastic and that people slide round on the sexual orientation continuum for all sorts of reasons.

Society's thinking about homosexuality and genetics
is very sloppy. Homosexuality has been labelled genetic,
fixed, and unchangeable for reasons that have nothing
to do with science.

What this book proves about any human behavior,
and certainly about homosexuality, is, "You can be that
way if you want to be, but you don't have to be if you
don't want to."

Human behavior is determined by both nature and
nurture. Without genes, you can't act in the environment
at all. But without the environment your genes have
nothing on which to act. No behavior, including homosexuality, results solely from genes. For homosexuality,
this book argues that the level of genetic influence could
easily be as low as 10 percent, the balance coming from
the environment. For other human behaviors, genetic
influence may be as high as 50 percent, but nothing
about that is fated either. Probably the best tool for
measuring genetic influence on any behavior—studies of
identical twins—makes it quite clear that the genetic influence of any behavior drops commensurately with whatever environmental interventions of an opposite kind
are brought to bear upon it. In other words, even if
homosexuality was 50% due to genes, opposite environmental influences could almost nullify it.

My Genes Made Me Do It! attempts to bring scientific
objectivity into the debate about homosexual orientation
and its many implications. There should be compassion,
but a false compassion based on ignorance of science is
about as kind to the homosexual, in the end, as someone
who smiles lovingly at you while he laces your coffee with
arsenic.

Notes

1. Levinson, S., Heen, W., and Burns, J., Should Hawaii Allow Same-Sex Marriage? *The Honolulu Advertiser* (9 May 1993): B1, B4.

2. Cameron P., *Exposing the AIDS Scandal* (Lafayette, LA: Huntington House Publishers, 1988).

Chapter One

Can Genes Create Sexual Preferences?

If I really wanted to get to know you, would it help if you offered me an analysis of your DNA? Or a chunk of your cellular fat and carbohydrate? Would an understanding of the way your genes produced the protein in your fingernails help me figure out why you bite them when you're nervous? Would the configuration of the nitrogenous bases in your DNA help me understand why you have a preference for *cordon bleu* on Tuesdays? Is it the chemistry of the paint that makes Rembrandt's *Self Portrait* what it is? Is it vibrational physics that makes Beethoven's *Symphony No 7* so magnificent?

These questions are ridiculous. If we wanted to be contentious, we could argue that the chemistry of paint and vibrational physics adds something to the portrait and the symphony. But most of us would say they don't have much to do with it. Mainstream geneticists react in much the same way when people try to argue human behavior—particularly, for the purposes of this book, homosexual behavior—is determined by genes. Most argue that environment has a very important part to play.

Some Fundamentals of Genetics

This chapter makes it clear that environmental factors are the predominant influence in sexual behavior and suggests that the people we ultimately become can hardly be hinted at from genetic structure and function.

But first, let's visit the nucleus of a single human cell for a moment and look at some of the fundamentals of genetics.

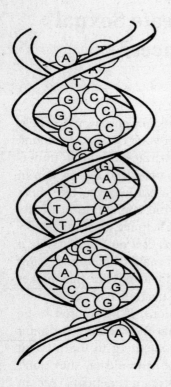

Figure 1:
One strand of DNA

If we pick any nucleus at random from one of the cells in our bodies, almost all of us will find forty-six chromosomes inside, forty-six microscopic squiggles of deoxyribonucleic acid (DNA). Each chromosome is made up of a highly folded strand of DNA, which forms a wondrous twisted ladder with 60 to 185 million rungs. If you joined, end to end, each unraveled chromosome in a single cell you'd have about three billion rungs.[1] That's a lot of rungs! If you climbed each rung at the rate of one a second, sixteen hours a day, it would take about two lifetimes to get to the top, and if you unrolled all the tightly coiled DNA in a single chromosome in a single human cell it would be as long as you are. Groups of the rungs comprise what we call genes. Genes are typically anything from 1600 to 4000 rungs long, but about 90 percent of the spiral ladder contains no genes; science does not yet know the function of these "waste" stretches of DNA.

The rungs are actually chemical bonds between what are called "nitrogenous bases" at the ends of the rungs.

These bases are various combinations of carbon, nitrogen, oxygen, and hydrogen, and look something like a rather skewed infinity symbol. In DNA, there are only four bases, with exotic names; thymine and adenine always join together to form one type of rung, and guanine and cytosine always form the other type of rung. One rung might be adenine and thymine (AT) and the next rung the same again, or thymine and adenine (TA), or cytosine and guanine (CG), or guanine and cytosine (GC). The ladder sides, between the rungs, are sugars! The sequence of rungs (that is, how many bases and in what sequence) represents special coded information called the genetic code, and it is this code which determines the transfer of hereditary information from one generation of cells to the next and from one generation of humans to the next. Scientists currently guess everyone has nearly 100,000 genes.[1]

The biochemistry in the nucleus also makes a copy of the gene: a secondary, smaller, slightly different, and more mobile piece of nucleic acid called ribonucleic acid (RNA), which is transferred out of the cell nucleus into the "body" of the cell where more biochemical machinery then uses it as a template to make specific proteins.

What the Gene Really Does

The gene's function is biochemical. The DNA contains a genetic code that spells out the instructions for making proteins: one gene for one protein. In fact, the process DNA>RNA>Protein is so basic to genetics that it has been called the *Central Dogma of Biochemistry*. Proteins are made up of various combinations of about twenty little molecules, called amino acids. Each group of three bases (triplets) on the ladder is a code specifying one individual amino acid which should link with those from the immediately adjacent triplets to form a protein. For example, the base triplet GTA codes for the amino acid histidine, while GTT codes for glutamine. The sequence, types, and numbers of amino acids largely determine the nature of the proteins.

If the DNA is correctly "read" and its recipe precisely followed, the "right" proteins will be produced in the cell and the gene will have been "expressed." If, however, the process is blocked, either through biological accident or through normal feedback mechanisms at higher levels, the gene is said to have been "repressed." In simple organisms, most genes are expressed, but, in complex organisms, only about 10-15 percent are expressed in any one organ. For example, genes coding for proteins involved in the development and function of the eye will be repressed in cells in the region of the toenail. The pattern of proteins produced depends on the pattern of repression.

Some of the proteins are also enzymes, which act as catalysts in chemical reactions producing more proteins, carbohydrates, and lipids (fats) from smaller components: amino acids, simple sugars (such as glucose), and fatty acids. Biochemists themselves rarely appreciate how complex a single cell is. One single fertilized ovum, for example, resembles a vast plain crammed with about a billion dancing figures on a complex grid, either spinning alone or briefly forming long chains or small groups or circles only to break away and form thousands of others. There are about one billion biochemical reactions each second within this single cell*—a dazzlingly complex mesh of actions, interactions, reactions, feedback and control paths, and co-operation and interference, causing thousands of genes, and all the gene-products within the cell, to interact. More than 100 trillion other cells in the human body have yet to develop in the same way and begin to interact with each other in this extraordinary dance of life.

---

* This was calculated from the energy used by a typical cell compared with the energy of a typical chemical bond.

Some people argue that genetic function goes much further than physiology—to human behavior. The spectrum of belief is wide, ranging from the many geneticists who believe that there is some genetic influence on human behavior to sociobiologists who hold that all human behavior is genetically predestined, coded into the genes. Some researchers have sought to find a link between genes and homosexuality. We'll look in detail at some of these arguments in later chapters, but right now let's look at basic genetics and see what general statements can be made about genetic influence and determinism in relation to sexual behavior.

No gene can do anything by itself

"Researcher finds gay gene" was the way one capital city newspaper headlined the news of Dr. Dean Hamer's claim to have found a link between genetics and homosexuality a few years ago (see Chapter 9). But that's not what Dean Hamer was claiming, at least publicly. Dr. Hamer said: "We have not found the gene—which we don't think exists—for sexual orientation."[2] Hamer knows that any attempt to argue the existence of a "homosexual gene", a single, apparently autocratic, gene governing homosexuality, is nonsense, genetically. There is no single gene governing sexual preference or any other preference. There is no gene for smoking, dancing, or making sarcastic remarks.

Why is this so? Because, for a gene to even be expressed, it has to be acted upon by the products of another expressed gene or genes. It probably takes combinations of products from at least five separate genes, and sometimes as many as twenty separate genes, to activate a single gene in a single cell into expressing itself.[3] The products may come from some obscure part of the molecular dance or sometimes from outside the cell. No gene is an island—it interacts with other genes in a kind of ecology in which it is almost impossible for any one gene, or a minor combination of genes to completely control all the others, though a group of genes does determine (usually) the body form and organization of organs in the body and the expression of all other genes during development. The simple world of Gregor Mendel and his peas—in which single traits like tallness, color, and seed shape are each determined by a single gene— is almost never seen in human genetics.

Hamer would have been happier if he had found several interacting genes.

Any behavior links are with many genes

If you're going to argue that human sexual behavior is dictated, or influenced by, genes in any way, many genes are involved.

In very simple organisms, one or two genes govern simple behaviors. Researchers found that, when certain genes were repressed or disabled in some way in an offspring, a certain behavior suddenly disappeared. For example, the sandhopper's feeding behavior is dependent on a single gene which produces an enzyme that breaks down complex sugars into simple, sweet sugars. Different sandhoppers have different genes, which produce different enzymes, which break down different complex sugars. So, different sandhoppers have different favorite foods because they go for different complex sugars. But, if the gene producing that particular enzyme is disabled or repressed in the offspring of a particular sandhopper, that generation is no longer so interested in its parents' favorite food.[4]

It has become a genetic truism that if simple organisms in selective breeding experiments that repress or eliminate a particular gene or genes, lose in the next couple of generations a clearly defined, consistent behavior, then that behavior can be said to be governed by that gene or those few genes. The same is true if the gene (or genes) is (are) expressed or restored in the organism in the next couple of generations, and the behavior returns.

This means the converse is also true: when a behavior is being selectively bred in over many generations, and changes are slow and steady, many genes are responsible. One of the longest studies on mammalian behavior ever undertaken was done on thirty generations of mice.[5] Thirty generations is equivalent to about 1000 years of selective human breeding. The mice were deliberately bred to create two strains of behavior: activity and passivity, tested by aversion to intense light. Those which reacted strongly were active, those which didn't react so strongly were passive. Active mice were then mated with active, and passive with passive, and the offspring re-tested. What happened was a slow, steady and gradual change of behavior over 30 generations: the active mice became more active and the passive became more passive, until their activity could not be distinguished from zero. Similar results have been found in mice bred for alcohol sensitivity, preference, and withdrawal; various types of learning; exploratory behavior abilities; aggressiveness; and nest building.

A well known behavioral genetics expert, Plomin, has commented about this gradual change of behavior: "Th(is) steady divergence . . . provides the best available evidence that many genes affect behavior." Drawing on other studies, he said that if only one or two genes had been involved, the mice would have sorted themselves abruptly into one or other of the two groups within just a few generations. Other geneticists concur with Plomin. When there are slow shifts in behavior with each generation (as in the breeding of dogs for specific behaviors), they believe that many genes are interacting—probably hundreds of genes—with each contributing a tiny part of the whole effect.

Moving from mice and dogs to humans, this effect is also clear if we look at IQ. We know that many more than 100 genes are involved in IQ in humans because at least 100 separate gene defects are already known to individually lower IQ.[6]

In the active/passive mice experiment there was also a control group of mice—a group that was left alone to breed randomly over the same thirty generations. What happened to that group? There was no significant change in behavior. At any one time, the behavior of those mice was about the average of that in the active and passive groups. As in the active/passive groups, there were no sudden random fluctuations of behavior, as there would have been had the behavior been controlled by only a few genes. This principle holds true if we look at any broad continuum of behavior found at any one time in any population (e.g., a survey of any Western population will reveal all the shades of sexual preference from exclusive heterosexuality through various shades of bisexuality to exclusive homosexuality). Geneticists say that this continuum is evidence that there are at least several (five-seven) genes involved. However, as we will find further on in this chapter, it makes no difference to our main argument if some behaviors are ultimately found to be associated with only a handful of genes. It still holds true that sexual behavior is not genetically dictated.

Implications for sexual behavior of "many genes"

If, when many genes are involved, changes in behavior take place very slowly, over very many generations, how can homosexuality suddenly appear as it does in a family? The only way it could would be for many recessive "homosexual" genes to switch on spontaneously and simultaneously very early in the life of the fetus, and all the "heterosexual" genes to completely switch off. This is extremely unlikely. If many genes were involved the typical genetic pattern would be a gradual change in the family toward homosexuality—a few percent with each generation over the course perhaps thirty generations. Similarly, homosexuality would only slowly disappear in the descendants (if any) of a homosexual person. Any other proposed mechanism is highly speculative.

Behaviors which do change slowly over the generations in a family or society are much more likely to be genetically influenced or determined, but homosexuality changes too swiftly to be genetically controlled or influenced by many genes.

Could homosexuality be a result of mutation?

It's highly unlikely the gay community would accept such an explanation, but from a biological point of view, could homosexuality possibly be the result of a mutation?

What causes a mutation? It can be something as simple as one wrong DNA triplet code in a critical place. The effect might be like a plane crashing in the middle of the group of dancers. They may form new circles and groups to try to compensate for the deaths of their companions, but things will never be the same again.

There are many conditions now known to scientists that have been traced to specific single gene locations or chromosome faults: muscular dystrophy, familial colon cancer, Huntington's disease, cystic fibrosis, sickle cell anemia, Down's syndrome, hemochromatosis (abnormally high storage of iron from the diet), multiple exotoses (a disorder of cartilage and bone), haemophilia, polycystic kidney disease, Lou Gehrigs's disease (fatal degenerative nerve ailment), and neurofibromatosis. These are physical conditions resulting from breakdown of biological processes, or faults in genes. They are not behaviors, though distinctive behaviors may result from them—as in Down's syndrome (simple behavior). Plomin claims more than 4000 gene effects due to mutation are known in the human organism—most of them creating the kinds of physical defects just mentioned.[5] But attempts by scientists to pin specific behaviors down to single gene defects or specific genes are proving very difficult and unproductive. The only genetic links to behavior have been very dubiously established and usually only link to negative behaviors (see Chapter 9), and most of these findings have been retracted in the face of the repeated failure of further independent laboratory tests.

Let's look at one of the of the most direct results of
mutation on human behavior known so far and examine
the implications. It's a rare condition associated with
aggression, in a study of Dutch men,[7] and is probably an
example of the maximum genetic contribution to a behavior you are likely to see. People without the condition
have an enzyme in their bodies called monoamine oxidase A, which performs a simple oxidation of basic com-
pounds called amines. Dutch men affected with the syndrome completely lack the active enzyme, because a genetic mutation has made a minor change to one of the
amino acids making up the enzyme. The defective gene
is passed on by the mother and also creates borderline
mental retardation. Alleged behavioral symptoms include
aggression, arson, attempted rape, and exhibitionism—
behaviors that were described as "disturbed regulation of
impulsive aggression."

The aggressive behavior in the Dutch men varied
greatly over time and in type, and—according to the
authors—could have been linked to levels of fear, anger,
and frustration, possibly related to the borderline mental retardation that is part of the syndrome. Significantly,
experiments using drugs to specifically inhibit the production of this enzyme in normal adults have not raised
levels of aggression. Also, the condition arising from the
mutation was easily controllable: after counselling the
men were able to lead virtually normal lives and their
antisocial behavior almost disappeared. The variation in
behavior, the lack of change in aggression levels in normal adults despite inhibition of the enzyme, and changes
after counselling disprove a genetically dictated aggression.

Another well-known genetic mutation, phenylketonuria, ultimately causes mental retardation. This is
the result of a lack of one particular enzyme which adds
oxygen to the amino acid phenylalanine. Enzymes often
act in series, forming a pathway, and the entire pathway

may block if one of its members is not there and there are no good bypass routes. This is what happens in phenylketonuria. But environmental intervention can get around the problem entirely. In the case of phenylketonuria, which causes retardation in a high percentage of cases, the affected person simply avoids phenylalanine in his diet. This environmental intervention is 100 percent effective.

So–what are we saying?

• We are saying that one of the most closely genetically-linked human behaviors known to science is certainly not determined. This raises the question: Is there any such thing as a genetically determined human behavior?

• We are saying that even if behaviors are linked (not dictated by, but linked) to genes, environmental interventions (e.g., diet, counseling) can greatly modify or even eliminate the behavior (see chapter ten). As Plomin remarks, "If a certain form of psychopathology should be caused primarily by genes it might be mistakenly assumed that psychotherapy and other environmental intervention would be useless. This pessimistic point of view is simply wrong."[6]

But, specifically, homosexuality would appear not to be caused by mutation. Why not?

• Just as many "homosexual" genes would suddenly have to switch on and off if the sudden appearance and disappearance of homosexuality in families is to be accounted for, so, many genes would suddenly have to mutate if we want to argue that homosexuality is caused by mutation. The chances that even ten genes might spontaneously change from "heterosexual" to "homosexual" by mutation is much less than one in a thousand, and geneticists would find it inconceivable that hundreds of genes could do so.

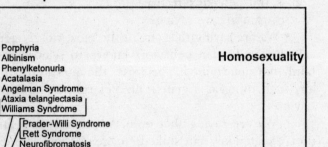

Figure 2: Population Incidence of Genetic Disorders

• There is another difficulty with the mutation theory. Most conditions caused by mutations affect only a very small proportion of the general population: about 0.025 percent of the population or less, in each case. Altogether, conditions caused by genetic mutation are found in about only 1 percent of the total population.[8, 9] Homosexuality, with its total incidence (2.2 percent), does not fit plausibly into the category of genetic diseases because its incidence is far too high (see Figure 2, data taken from PEDINFO on the Internet at http://w3.lhl.uab.edu). It fits much more naturally into the category of psychological disturbances and disorders, which are common by comparison (see Figure 3).[10]

Incidence of Psychological Symptoms

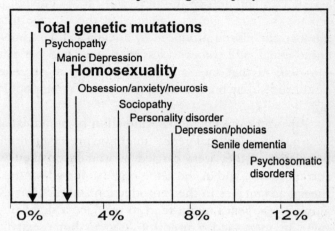

Figure 3: Incidence of Psychological Symptoms

How could genetic homosexuality maintain itself in the population?

There is another objection to the notion of a genetically induced homosexuality. An unreproductive behavior cannot be genetically enforced and also continue to exist in the population. According to mainstream genetics, genetically enforced homosexuality (exclusively same-sex sex) would die out of the population in several generations.

Here's how. A gene is retained in the gene pool when an average of at least one child is born to every adult having that gene (one child per person). As unlikely as it sounds, surveys show that of persons classifying themselves as exclusively homosexual, one in five has a child. At that rate, a homosexual gene, or genes, could not be replaced.

But most homosexuals are married (see Chapter Two). Wouldn't this preserve any homosexual gene or genes? Not necessarily. A married homosexual is usually bisexual. According to surveys, bisexuals have an average of 1.25 children each. On its own, that's enough to replace the adult gene or genes, but the average total number of children produced by bisexuals and exclusive homosexuals still comes to less than one child per person—0.9. At that rate, any homosexual gene or genes would still slowly but inevitably breed out of the population.

Advocates of genetic determination of homosexuality argue "homosexual genes" might be preserved in the population if they were carried by women on their X-chromosomes, and at the same time conferred on them special advantages in the reproduction stakes.[11] For example these genes might tend to produce a slight physique in men—and a predisposition to homosexuality through the social effects detailed in chapter three—but the same genes in women would tend to produce a petite, possibly more feminine woman, more attractive to men. But this is highly speculative and sits uneasily with what little evidence we do have. Male homosexuals are often of strong physique, and mothers of homosexual males are not noticeably ultra-feminine.

Sociobiologists, almost the only group of academics who argue seriously that all human behavior is preordained by genes, have great difficulty accounting for the persistence of homosexuality in the population. They try to argue that genes causing male homosexuality would also exist in the sisters of gays, and that the homosexual male would help ensure those genes were passed on by helping his sister and her family—for example, babysitting, and later helping with money and resources. But these arguments are unusually weak. On average, homosexuals tend not to have close relationships with their biological families.[12]

Summary

No mainstream geneticist is happy with the idea that genes dictate behavior, particularly homosexual behavior.

- No genetically determined human behavior has yet been found. The most closely genetically-related behavior yet discovered has shown itself remarkably responsive to counselling.
- Genetically dictated behavior is something that has so far been discovered only in very simple organisms.
- If homosexuality were genetically determined, it would have bred itself out of the population in only several generations, and wouldn't be around today.
- From an understanding of gene structure and function there are no plausible means by which genes could inescapably force homosexuality or other behaviors on a person. Genes make proteins, not preferences.

Generally, geneticists settle for some genetic influence of rather undefined degree, most agreeing that many genes (from at least five or six to many hundreds) contribute to human behavior. But they are uneasy about a direct genetic contribution to homosexuality.

- A genetically dominated homosexuality could not suddenly appear and disappear in families. It would stay around for many generations.

In the following chapters we will attempt to be much more precise about the level of genetic contribution to homosexuality.

Gays tend to back whatever current research might be useful in the campaign for gay rights, but the words of one gay activist are probably closer to the truth. The genetic argument was an "expedient lie", he said.[13]

In the years ahead more genetic links with behaviors will probably be found, but in no case will these determine that one is homosexual, or brilliant, or musical, or a reader of *My Genes Made Me Do It!* Whatever you might think about your behavior, the facts are, your genes did not make you do it.

Beloved . . . it does not yet appear what we shall be

Human beings start out as genes and biochemical processes. We develop into mature organisms. We end up as creatures with transcendent spiritual potential. We get there via a steadily ascending flight of steps which start at the genetic level.

Animals

At every stage between the genetic code and the mature organism, all the other influences (anything which is not the gene itself) are continuously interacting in a multitude of ways to create new and higher levels of chemical interaction and development, each further and further removed from genetic control and not predictable from it. Genes and biochemical processes comprise the first steps. At a higher level, cells interact with each other (e.g., a macrophage cell recognizes non-body cells and devours them). At a higher level still, the organs react with one another. Higher still, the animal as a whole reacts to the environment. Probably the apex of animal development is learning from the environment. Learning is perhaps half a dozen levels up from the basic chemistry and almost independent of it.

So the influence of genes is indirect, creating an organism which has huge potential to react and change in response to the environment, but not specifying many of the details, which are learned. A wild horse primed by its adrenal glands to bolt when it meets loud, fast-moving vehicles can be taught to plod through traffic without fear, and the learning is another environmental influence even more remote from the genes. So, even animals become beings which transcend their DNA because we can teach them. Monkeys can be taught a simple sign language for communication. Were the details of that language predictable from their DNA? Of course not. Humans taught it to the monkeys themselves. It came from completely outside them.

Humans

If the mature animal cannot be entirely predicted from its genes, human beings are light years removed from the control of a series of nitrogenous bases. In human development, as in the higher animals, each stage of development is hardly predictable from the previous stage, and each is further removed from the direct influence of genes. As the trillions of human cells of the body form, differentiate, and interact, they are already developing away from genetic control. (Stillbirth resulting from an inadequate supply of food and oxygen to the placenta is an example of a non-genetic birth defect from this stage.) At the level where organs are developing and working together harmoniously, genetic control is even more remote (e.g., a heart rate varies in response to emergencies in the environment, but if it were under direct genetic control, it would be constant).

The more complex the animal, the more it is possible to learn. Some foxes have learned to lie—to give false warning barks when no danger threatens, so other foxes will scatter and leave them with the prey. But human lying is extremely sophisticated, definitely learned, and out-foxes foxes! Humans learn about their environment as animals do, but at a speed and level far surpassing animals. Humans also develop greatly increased self consciousness and move on to master language and a galaxy of concepts, to create extraordinary things. They step up to another dimension of the spirit and God. How many levels is that? The precise number really doesn't matter. What does matter is that the highest levels are not predictable even in principle. Was it predictable from his genes that Jesus would say, "I am in the Father and you are in Me?"

Geneticists G.S. Omenn and A.G. Motulksy said, when they talked about the difficulties of predicting behavior from gene structure: "The hopelessness of understanding behavior from simple analytical approaches can be compared to the hopelessness of seeking linguistic insights by a chemical analysis of a book."[14]

Does this mean there is no genetic influence at all on our behavior? No. This chapter argues that we are creatures of genes and environment, but that for most behaviors, environment easily predominates or can be made to, by training and learning. We start our lives forced to climb the wondrous ladder of our genes. We make and design the ladders we climb in our environments. Finally, if we will, we can choose to climb another wondrous spiral staircase, one that leads us into the presence of God, where our genetic origins are completely transcended.

Notes

1. Lewin, B., *Genes V.* (Oxford: Oxford University Press, 1994).

2. McKie, R., "The Myth of the Gay Gene," *The Press* (NZ: 30 July 1993): 9.

3. Beardsley, T., "Smart Genes," *Scientific American,* 265 (February): 73-81.

4. Borowski, R., *BBC Science Magazine* (6 September 1993).

5. Plomin, R., "The Role of Inheritance in Behavior," *Science,* 248 (1990): 183-188.

6. Plomin, R., De Fries, J.C., McClearn, G.E., *Behavioral Genetics—A Primer* (San Francisco: W.H. Freeman, 1980).

7. Brunner, H.G., Nelen, M., Breakefield, X.O., Ropers, H.H., van Oost, B.A., "Abnormal behavior associated with a point mutation in the structural gene for monoamine oxidase A.," *Science* (1993) 262:578-580.

8. Cooper, D.N., Krawczak, M., *Human Gene Mutation,* (Oxford: Bios Scientific Publishers, 1993).

9. Cavalli-Sforza, L.L., Bodmer, W.F., *The Genetics of Human Populations* (San Francisco: W.H. Freeman, 1971).

10. Kessler, R.C., McGonagle, K.A., Zhao, S., Nelson, C.B., Hughes, M., Eshleman, S., Wittchen, H.U., Kendler, K.S., "Lifetime and 12-month prevalence of DSM-III-R

psychiatric disorders in the United States," *Archives of General Psychiatry* (1994) 51:8-19.

11. Burr, C., *A Separate Creation* (London: Bantam, 1996).

12. Cleveland, P.H., Walters, L.H., Skeen, P., Robinson, B.E., "If your child had AIDS . . . : responses of parents with homosexual children," *Family Relations* (1988) 37:150-153.

13. Anon., "Are Homosexuals Born That Way?" *Nation* (October 1992) 19:424-429.

14. Fausto-Sterling, A., *Myths of Gender* (New York: Basic Books Inc., 1985).

Chapter Two

The Genetic Implications of Homosexual Incidence

In the eighties and early nineties, it was widely put about that homosexuals were about one in ten of the population. The strongest proponents of the "one-in-ten" figure were gay activists who used it to give impetus to the drive for gay rights. Hard on the heels of the "one in ten" theory came the "gay is inborn" theory. The two worked together to accomplish considerable changes in attitudes of legislatures, churches, and society in general. If it can be shown that a group of people constituting such a large proportion of the population is being discriminated against for something it can do very little about (like skin color), then any decent individual will tend to concede it needs special protections.

It is not yet widely appreciated that the one-in-ten figure is a myth. Rather than lending support to arguments for genetic origins to homosexuality, the true incidence of homosexuality does the opposite.

So how did the "one-in-ten" myth begin? In 1948 and 1953, sex researcher Dr. Alfred Kinsey published two volumes called *Sexual Behavior in the Human Male*[1] and *Sexual Behavior in the Human Female.*[2] Among Kinsey's many claims was this one: 13 percent of men and 7 percent of women in his study were more or less homosexual for "at least three years between the ages of 16 and 55." Kinsey said the figures represented measurements of "psychologic response" and/or "homosexual experience"—that is, homosexual fantasy and same-sex contact to orgasm. The claim received huge media exposure.

Bruce Voeller, an associate professor at Rockefeller University and a non-practising homosexual added the 13 percent and the 7 percent together and concluded that "*an average of 10% of the population could be designated as Gay* . . . As a scientist I could see how handy it was to use the 10% figure."[3] Voeller, thereafter, became openly gay and was a founder of the modern gay activist movement. He used the figure to drive the campaign for recognition and acceptance.

> As I became a national Gay leader I insisted to other Gay leaders that we needed to bring the message(s) . . . home to the media, to judges and legislators, to ministers and rabbis, to psychiatrists. . . . I campaigned with Gay groups across the country for the Kinsey-based finding that "We are everywhere". This slogan became a National Gay Taskforce *leitmotiv*. And the issues became key parts of (our) national, political, educational and legislative programs. . . . After years of our educating those who inform the public and make its laws, the concept that 10% of the population is gay has become a generally accepted "fact" . . . the 10% figure is regularly utilized by scholars, by the press, and in government statistics. As with so many pieces of knowledge (and myth), repeated telling made it so.[4]

The problem was that Kinsey's figures were about four times too high.

What was wrong with Kinsey's work?

• It was heavily biased towards unrepresentative populations. Kinsey made no attempt to avoid a sample heavily weighted toward promiscuity and deviancy. His total male sample of 5300 comprised several hundred male prostitutes, 1200 convicted sex offenders, 300 students from a high school renowned for its "aberrant" (homosexual) sexuality, and high numbers of pedophiles and exhibitionists. Prison inmates, who are disproportionately homosexually active, comprised a quarter of his sample.

• He did not use random sampling. He used only volunteers. The "volunteer effect" in surveys on sexuality is known to bring forward people whose sexual behaviors are atypical. Though the effect is less visible in sexuality surveys today, it was marked forty years ago. American psychologist, Dr. Abraham Maslow, who initially collaborated with Kinsey, was convinced that those who volunteered for Kinsey's survey were more sexually adventurous, and he set out to test his hypothesis on five of his classes, many of whom were interviewed by Kinsey. He demonstrated clear volunteer bias in the student sample.

> As I expected, the volunteer error was proven and the whole basis for Kinsey's statistics was shown to be shaky. But he refused to publish it and refused to even mention it in his books, or to mention anything else that I had written. All my work was excluded from his bibliography.[5]

Kinsey claimed he eliminated volunteer bias by interviewing all of most groups studied, but his co-workers later said his actual rate was often as low as 35 percent.

• He included teenagers among those who had been "more or less homosexual for at least three years." This is an unreasonable categorization; sexual orientation in adolescents is still very fluid; sexual identity is still stabilizing.

• Kinsey measured homosexuality on the basis of fantasy and/or sexual experience. Limited sexual experience with someone of the same sex is not a good test of male homosexuality. Numbers of heterosexual men have male sex for a number of reasons: curiosity, for a dare,

because they are drunk, or because they are forced while
drunk or asleep, because the urge for sexual release
makes the gender of the partner temporarily irrelevant.

• Kinsey had an ideological agenda. Paul Robinson,
a historian and one of Kinsey's biographers, remarks
"Kinsey assigned [prominence] to masturbation and
homosexuality, both of which were objects of his
partiality . . . [He had a] tendency to conceive of the ideal
sexual universe according to the homoerotic model;"[4, 5]
Kinsey was bisexual and was deliberately trying to change
the moral climate in the U.S., although he maintained
his only motive was scientific objectivity.[5a] Reisman and
Fink also challenge the research methods that obtained
claimed orgasms from hundreds of children and infants.[4]

The data are therefore quite suspect. Some of the
best statistical investigators in the world—Cochran,
Mosteller, Tukey—commenting on the male and female
reports, agree that the procedures adopted by Kinsey
and his team inflated the homosexual figures.

Modern Surveys

By the mid nineties, more than thirty surveys of homosexual incidence were based on genuinely represen-
tative samples, mostly from Western countries (see Figures 4 to 7, and p.39 footnote.)

The heavy dashed line in all four figures represents
the mean, and the lighter dashed lines the standard
deviations, which include about two thirds of the points.
Individual points have error bars which are one standard
deviation, as estimated from the sample size.

Figure 4 shows the percentage of bisexuality and
exclusive homosexuality among western adult males,
Figure 5 the percentage of bisexuality and exclusive lesbianism among adult females in the West.

Male sexual orientation

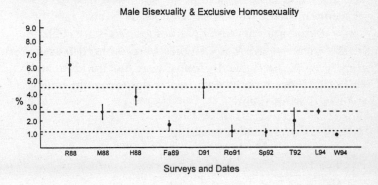

Figure 4: Male Sexual Orientation

Female sexual orientation.

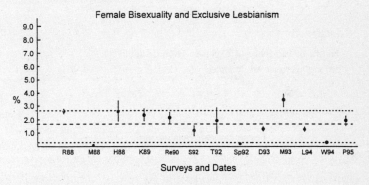

Figure 5: Female Sexual Orientation

Figures 6 and 7 show the percentage of exclusive adult homosexuality and lesbianism in mostly Western nations. The surveys are randomized within the study countries and record by sexual contact, people who have always been exclusively homosexual or those exclusively homosexual in the twelve months before the survey. This is a rather restrictive definition, but there is little disagreement about what it represents. It is also fair, because few people identifying as homosexuals are celibate in any given year.[6] Many studies were omitted because they were of specialized groups, were not randomized, or because the type of data in the figures could not be extracted from them.

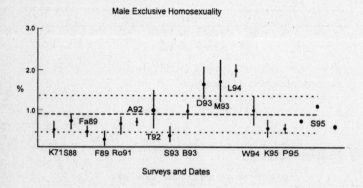

Figure 6: Incidence of Exclusive Homosexuality among Western Adult Males

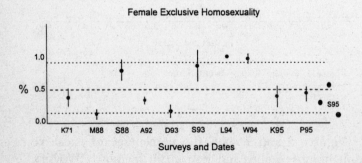

Figure 7: Incidence of Exclusive Lesbianism

About 1 percent of the adult male population is exclusively homosexual,[7] and about 0.5 percent of the adult female population is exclusively lesbian at any given time—a grand mean of 0.7 percent of the total adult population. (Or, to put it more accurately, the incidence of exclusively homosexual activity among Western adults in any given year is 0.9 ± 0.1 percent of men and 0.5 ± 0.1 percent of women. If bisexuality is included the figure rises to 2.7 ± 1.7 percent for men and 1.7 ± 1.0 percent for women.*) Around 2.2 percent of the total adult population is homosexual, lesbian, or bisexual. Homosexual incidence is nowhere near one in ten of the population.

Most Homosexuals are Married

The surveys of bisexual incidence come up with an interesting statistic. Of all homosexually active males, about 55 percent are married (which is the average of a range of surveys finding between 25 percent to 80 percent), and the true figure is likely to be toward the upper end of the scale because married homosexual men tend to refuse to answer such surveys.[7-11] In most cases, wives are ignorant of their husbands' homosexual behavior.

A 1970 Kinsey Institute survey of females shows lesbianism somewhat resembles the male pattern: about 45 percent of lesbians have been married, and about 45 percent are currently married. About 10 percent are single.[12]

These are important statistics because they suggest that a significant amount of bisexuality is, in fact, homo-

---

*Figure Four (Male bisexuality and Exclusive Homosexuality): R88,[13] M88,[14] H88,[15] Fa89,[10] D91,[16] Ro91,[17] Sp92,[18] T92,[19] L94,[7] W94.[20] Figure Five (Female Bisexuality and Exclusive Homosexuality): R88,[13] M88,[14] H88,[21] K89,[12] Re90,[22] S92,[23] T92,[19] Sp92,[18] D93,[15] M93,[15] L94,[7] W94,[20] P95.[24] Figure Six (Male Exclusive Homosexuality): K71,[25] S88,[26] Fa89,[10] F89,[27] Ro91,[17] A92,[28] T92,[19] S93,[23] B93,[29] D93,[15] M93,[15] L94,[7] W94,[20] K95,[25] P95,[24] S95.[30] Figure Seven (Female Exclusive Homosexuality): K71,[25] M88,[14] S88,[26] A92,[28] D93,[15] S93,[23] L94,[7] W94,[20] K95,[25] P95,[24] S95.[30]

sexual behavior by married homosexual men and lesbians. We could probably say that most bisexuals are, in fact homosexuals and lesbians who are or have been married. But even the figure for bisexuality isn't anything near Kinsey's 10 percent.

Incidence and Genetics

The incidence of homosexuality has important implications for the nature/nature debate.

- Homosexual incidence is too high, even at only 1 percent, to be caused by genetic mutation. We showed in the last chapter (Figures 2 and 3), that most conditions caused by mutation each affect only about 0.025 percent of the population. Homosexuality fits much more naturally into that group of human behaviors which are psychological in nature.

- Homosexuality is not fixed. Although the Kinsey surveys of 1948 and 1953 greatly exaggerated homosexual and bisexual incidence, they showed one interesting trend, also borne out by subsequent studies—a steady decline in homosexual fantasy and activity with increasing age (see Figures 8 and 9). In other words, homosexual orientation and behavior is not a static condition. This has significant implications for arguments that homosexuality is genetically determined. Whatever is genetically determined is by definition, unable to change within a generation.

Kinsey Classes (Males)
1948

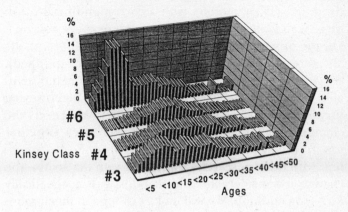

Figure 8:   Kinsey Class 6—Exclusively Homosexual,
Class 5—Predominantly Homosexual,
Class 4—Mostly Homosexual,
Class 3—Equally Homosexual & Heterosexual

Kinsey Classes (Women)
1953

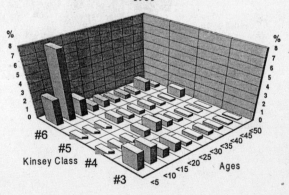

Figure 9:   Kinsey Class 6—Exclusively Homosexual,
Class 5—Predominantly Homosexual,
Class 4—Mostly Homosexual,
Class 3—Equally Homosexual & Heterosexual

Later studies[7] (Figures 10 and 11) also show a decrease in homosexual behavior, this time about four-fold
(from age 35 to age 55), with a corresponding drop in
those who *identify* themselves as homosexual or bisexual.
On the other hand, data from the Kinsey reports shows
an increase in heterosexuality with age (not graphed),
suggesting a change from homosexuality to heterosexuality with age, though Laumann et al. found heterosexual
incidence remained relatively stable. Wherever the
changed homosexual/bisexual behavior goes—whether
toward the heterosexual end of the Kinsey Scale (consistent with other research findings) or into inactivity—the
change is considerable, and at odds with a genetically
dictated condition. We will look at change in much more
detail in chapter twelve.

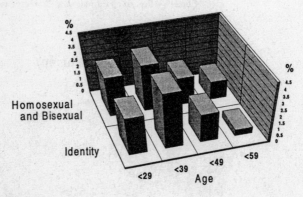

Men - Changes with age
Laumann 1994

Figure 10:

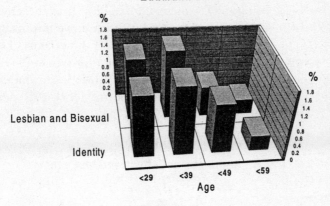

Women - Changes with age
Laumann 1994

Figure 11:

- Incidence studies argue for a high environmental influence in homosexuality. A large Chicago study[7] asked where people had been brought up during ages fourteen to sixteen years and whether they had any male homosexual partners during the last year. The percentages differed for different degrees of urbanization; 1.2 percent of the males surveyed who had been raised in rural areas reported having homosexual partners during the last year; 2.5 percent who had been raised in medium-sized towns reported having homosexual partners, and 4.4 percent who had been raised in large cities reported being active homosexuals (see Figure 12). For women, the percentages were 0.7 percent, 1.3 percent and 1.6 percent, respectively. In other words, *where you were brought up* is quite an important factor in whether you end up having homosexual partners. For the sake of argument, let us imagine that the incidence of male homosexuality in rural areas (1.2 percent) is all due to genetic influence. If that were the case, geneticists would also expect 1.2 percent of the male population in "big cities" to have a genetically based homosexuality, meaning that the homosexuality of the balance (3.2 percent) would be exclusively due to social factors. This means, for males, that the environmental factor (3.2 percent) is far more important than the alleged genetic factor (1.2 percent). For women the environmental factor (0.9 percent) [1.6 percent minus 0.7 percent], is slightly more important than the supposed genetic influence (0.7 percent).

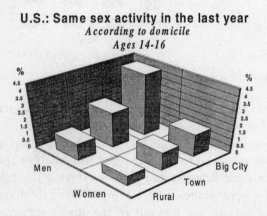

U.S.: Same sex activity in the last year
According to domicile
Ages 14-16

Figure 12:

In several other chapters we argue that it is entirely plausible that 90 percent of homosexuality is accounted for by environmental factors. This Chicago study supports that.

Conclusion

Homosexual incidence in Western adult populations is much lower than one in ten. About 0.9 percent of adult males are exclusively homosexual and about 0.5 percent of adult women are exclusively lesbian. The figure for bisexuality and exclusive homosexuality combined, rises to about 2.7 percent for males and 1.7 percent for females, an average of 2.2 percent of the total adult population. Much of the alleged bisexual component could comprise homosexuals and lesbians who are or have been married, but, even then, the figure falls far short of Kinsey's 10 percent.

Both Kinsey's figures and modern incidence surveys support a greater environmental contribution to homosexuality than a genetic one. People move away from homosexual behavior with age (meaning the condition cannot be genetically determined), the incidence is too high for homosexuality and bisexuality to sit easily in the genetic category, and even the strongest arguments in favor of genetic homosexuality still show that environmental factors are at least twice as strong in the development of homosexuality, and probably many times stronger.

Notes

1. Kinsey, A.C., Pomeroy, W.B., Martin, C.E., *Sexual Behavior in the Human Male* (Philadelphia: W.B. Saunders, 1948).

2. Kinsey, A.C., Pomeroy, W.B., Martin, C.E., Gebhard, P.H., *Sexual Behavior in the Human Female* (Philadelphia: W.B. Saunders, 1953).

3. Voeller, B., "Some uses and abuses of the Kinsey scale" In:. (Eds., McWhirter, D.P., Sanders, S.A., Reinisch, J.O.), *Homosexuality/Heterosexuality* (New York: Oxford University Press, 1990), 32-38.

4. Reisman, J.A., Eichel, E.W., (eds., Muir, J.G., Court, J.H.), *Kinsey, Sex, and Fraud* (Lafayette, LA: Lochinvar-Huntington House, 1990).

5. Robinson, P., *The Modernization of Sex* (New York: Harper and Row, 1976).

5a. Epstein, J., "The Secret Life of Alfred Kinsey," *Commentary* (January 1998): 35-39.

6. Brown, P., "Dangers of Monogamy," *New Scientist* (21 November 1992): 135:38-39.

7. Laumann, E.O., Gagnon, J.H., Michael, R.T., Michaels, S., *The Social Organization of Sexuality* (Chicago: University of Chicago Press, 1994).

8. Gebhard, P.H., Gagnon, J.H. Pomeroy, W.B., Christenson, C.V., *Sex Offenders, An Analysis of Types* (London: Heinemann, 1965).

9. Humphreys, L., *Tearoom Trade: Impersonal Sex in Public Places* (Chicago: Aldine, 1970).

10. Fay, R.E., Turner, C.F., Klassen, A.D., Gagnon, J.H. "Prevalence and patterns of same-gender sexual contact among men," *Science* (1989) 243, 338-348.

11. Ross, M.W., "Married homosexual men: prevalence and background," *Marriage and Family Review* (1990), 14:35-57.

12. Klassen, A.D., Williams, C.J., Levitt, E.E., *Sex and Morality in the U.S.* (Connecticut: Wesleyan University Press, 1989).

13. Ross, M.W. "Prevalence of risk factors for human immunodeficiency virus infection in the Australian population" *Medical Journal of Australia* (1988), 149:362-365.

14. Michael, R.T., Laumann, E.O., Gagnon, J.H., Smith, T.W., "Number of sex partners and potential risk of sexual exposure to human immunodeficiency virus," *Morbidity and Mortality Weekly Report* (1988), 37:565-568.

15. Diamond, M., "Homosexuality and bisexuality in different populations," *Archives of Sexual Behavior* (1993), 22:291-310.

16. Dixon, B.W., Streiff, E.J., Brunwasser, A.H., Haley, C.E., Freeman, A., Green, H.G., "Pilot study of a house-

hold survey to determine HIV seroprevalence," *Morbidity and Mortality Weekly Report* (1991), 40:1-5.

17. Rogers, S.M., Turner, C.F., "Male-male sexual contact in the USA: Findings from five sample surveys, 1970-1990." *The Journal of Sex Research* (1991), 28:491-519.

18. Spira, A., Bajos, N., Bejin, A., Beltzer, N., Bozon, M., Ducot, B., Durandeau, A., Ferrand, A., Giami, A., Gilloire, A., Giraud, M., Leridon, H., Messiah, A., Ludwig, D., Moatti, J.P., Mounnier, L., Olomucki, H., Poplavsky, J., Riandey, B., Spencer, B., Sztalryd, J.M., Touzard, H., *Les Comportments Sexuels en France.* (Paris: La Documentation Francaise, 1992).

19. Trocki, K.F., "Patterns of sexuality and risky sexuality in the general population of a California county," *The Journal of Sex Research* (1992), 29:85-94.

20. Wellings, K., Field, J., Johnson, A., Wadsworth, J., *Sexual Behavior in Britain: the National Survey of Sexual Attitudes and Lifestyles* (New York: Penguin, 1994).

21. *Harris Poll, Survey for Project Hope* (New York: Louis Harris and Associates, 1988).

22. Research Triangle Institute, *National household seroprevalence survey feasibility study final report. RTI report No. RTI/4190-01/01F* (North Carolina: Research Triangle Institute, Research Triangle Park, 1990).

23. Sittitrai, W., Brown, T., Virulrak, S., "Patterns of bisexuality in Thailand." In *Bisexuality and HIV/AIDS* edited by R. Tielman, M. Carballo and A. Hendricks (Buffalo, NY: Prometheus Books, 1992), 97-117.

24. Paul, C., Dickson, N., Davis, P.B., Yee, R.L., Chetwynd, J., McMillan, N., "Heterosexual behavior and HIV risk in New Zealand: data from a national survey," *Australian Journal of Public Health* (1995), 19:13-18.

25. Kontula, O., Haavio-Mannila, E., "Sexual Pleasures," *Enhancement of Sex Life in Finland, 1971-1992,* (Dartmouth, Aldershot, UK, 1995).

26. Sundet, J.M., Kvalem, I.L., Magnus, P., Bakketeig, L.S., "Prevalence of risk-prone sexual behavior in the general population of Norway." In *The Global Impact of AIDS* (New York: Alan R. Liss, 1988).

27. Forman, D., Chilvers, C., "Sexual behavior of young and middle aged men in England and Wales," *British Medical Journal* (1989), 298:1137-1142.

28. ACSF investigators, "AIDS and sexual behavior in France," *Nature* (1992), 360:407-409.

29. Billy, JOG, Tanfer, K., Grady, W.R., Klepinger, D.H., "The sexual behavior of men in the United States," *Family Planning Perspectives* (1993), 25:52-60.

30. Sell, R.L., Wells, J.A., Wypij, D., "The prevalence of homosexual behavior and attraction in the United States, the United Kingdom and France. Results of national population-based samples," *Archives of Sexual Behavior* (1995), 24:235-248.

Chapter Three

Are Heterosexuals Born that Way?

If anyone asked you how you became heterosexual, what would you say? You might shrug and say something like, "I don't know, it just happened. Maybe I was born that way?" But it's no mystery how we become heterosexual; the stages of human development toward heterosexuality are well known and documented, and in this chapter we'll look at the most important ones. Altogether they make a strong case for an environmental rather than a biological basis to sexuality. The research literature also gives good evidence that many people who have a homosexual orientation (whose sexual attraction is toward the same sex) missed out conspicuously in at least two stages critical to heterosexual development.

Stages of Heterosexual Development

Affection, Nurture and Bonding

A female fly lays eggs near food, but she is not around when the young grubs hatch. They have no family life, no mothering, no fathering. The presence of the female fly is not needed; the grubs do not need her affection, but still breed like, well . . . flies. On the other hand some of the higher animals particularly need early mothering. Affectionate early nurture seems to produce the capacity for affection in offspring—with effects on sexuality.

Researchers who have brought up monkeys completely isolated from other monkeys, giving them only a cloth mother figure, have found subsequent breakdown in their mating behavior.[1] When they were frightened, young male monkeys would run to the cloth figure and cling to it as a kind of substitute mother. But when they were mature and were introduced to sexually receptive females, they were confused, clumsy and fumbling in their attempts to mate, and frequently failed to do so when they tried. The researchers concluded that mating is not completely instinctive but partly learned, and depends on the quality of early nurturing. Female monkeys brought up without maternal nurture don't have such obvious trouble mating, but their behavior as mothers is alarming. They are brutal and even lethal mothers; "helpless, hopeless and heartless" the researchers observed,[1] a finding they extrapolated to abusive human parents. Early isolation and lack of nurturing fail to create affection in offspring. This affects the mating abilities of male monkeys and makes poor mothers of female monkeys.

What about us? Do we learn to be affectionate from our earliest relationships? It seems we probably do. Environments severely deprived of nurture don't just create people who are unable to be affectionate with either sex, they actually kill us.

The thirteenth century chronicler Salimbeni of Parma, Italy, told the story of Frederick II of Germany.[2] Frederick had extensive domains in Sicily and Italy, was "Holy Roman Emperor", and was considered perhaps the most enlightened man of his age. He was tolerant toward Jews and Muslims and a patron of the arts and sciences. (He was also reportedly "bald, red and short-sighted.") Frederick II had a theory that there was an original Adamic language, innate to all mankind, but that we did not grow up speaking it because we were exposed to the languages of our countries through our parents. He thought that if children were brought up in isolation they would automatically start speaking this original language. So he took some children and committed them to the care of nurses, but only for feeding and bathing.

There was to be no cuddling, caressing, or speaking. The children did not survive long enough to develop any language at all. They all died. (Frederick's reaction is not recorded but, he was so short-sighted he should have been red-faced, to put it baldly!)

In 1760, a Spanish bishop recorded: "in an orphanage children become sad, and many of them die because of this sadness". In those days an orphan child in an orphanage received minimal care and little affection.[2]

In their attempt to breed a master Aryan race, the Nazis took children born from genetically "ideal" parents and attempted to raise them under controlled conditions to realize their maximum potential. The directors of the program did not give the children normal mothering; they were left to their own devices in an institution for long periods. The experiment was a disaster. Again, some of the children died, and most of the rest developed severe psychological problems, which often left them unable to form normal relationships.

Langmeier, well-known for research into the effects of extreme isolation in early childhood, has found children deprived in this way are slow to develop generally, and find it difficult to form normal human relationships of all kinds.[2] Nielson, et al., looking at offending delinquent adolescents, found numbers of offences correlated with extent of early maternal separation. These children "lack basic human trust and capacity for empathy, and their interpersonal relationships are shallow."[3] In a classic paper, Helen Deutsch linked early loss of maternal nurture with lack of affection and inability to form relationships in adulthood.[4]

Beres and Obers (cited in Schwartz, et al.[1]) remark on the effects of severe deficiency in early maternal nurture. They followed thirty-eight subjects aged sixteen to twenty-eight who had been institutionalized early in life, and remarked that none of them "demonstrated the capacity to make a successful marriage or to parent." Beres and Obers thought this was primarily an intimacy problem. Another feature of some individuals with attachment problems is a total lack of fantasy. Some find any kind of imagination difficult.

In the 1950s, the World Health Organization asked British psychoanalyst John Bowlby to research the mental health of homeless children. His response was a monumental book, *Attachment and Loss,* which led to more affectionate childcare in institutions. Bowlby found that extreme emotional deprivation in early childhood produced children with very cold personalities who were unable to form lasting relationships. They also craved affection.[5]

In contrast, affection shown to baby boys (by anyone, but especially the mother) sometimes produces an erection. This undifferentiated response becomes more and more specific with age, eventually being restricted to those of the opposite sex who are potentially sexually responsive. This process of differentiation is connected with the development of gender identity.

Parental Gender Expectations and Training

Mothers often deny treating boys and girls differently, but studies show they do. The parents know the gender of the child and from then on treat him or her as a member of that sex—often unconsciously. Boys' limbs are exercised and stretched far more, and the vocal babblings of girls are imitated far more. Later in infancy, boys are allowed less physical contact and less verbal and eye contact than girls. Boys are more likely to be held facing away from the mother (and father) than toward. The parents are more likely to point something out to a boy than a girl. The mother tends to yield more often to the boy's demand to feed, whereas the girl is more readily denied and given direction. She has to yield to her mother's ideas of how much to take and when. When this sort of different behavior is repeated hundreds of times, it is bound to have an effect. "By the age of thirteen months, there are clear differences between male and female children," says LaTorre.[6] "There is apparently an attempt to "develop independence, adventure and mastery in the boy. . . . The males show much more exploratory and autonomous behavior."

Most other people also reflect their gender expectations toward the child. In some experiments, researchers took young babies and pinned opposite-sex names on them: girls names on boys and vice versa. Without knowledge of the experiment, people who were strangers to the babies were brought in to see them. Predictably, they cooed over the "girl" babies saying "Isn't she pretty?", and over the "boys" said things like, "Looks like he'll be a good cricket player when he grows up." A father, watching his young son tear into a steak with unsteady knife and fork, remarked approvingly, "That'll give you big muscles!" Presumably he would never have said it to his young daughter. If a little boy drops his trousers and piddles in the back garden, mother laughs tolerantly, but if her daughter takes off her underwear and throws it over the neighbor's fence, she is probably scolded. Studies again show that the boy is given much more freedom and allowed to do many things the girl is not. His dirtiness and untidiness is tolerated far more than a girl's.

The Growth of Gender-Awareness

Imitation is one of the child's main methods of learning. One of a baby's first milestones is the first smile, at about the age of ten weeks. When it is not indigestion, it may be an imitation of its mother's smile. At about five to seven months, a child knows the difference between Daddy and Mummy, and begins to turn to them for comfort and protection rather than strangers. At about the same time, a sense of "self" begins—children begin to realize that mirrors portray themselves as separate entities.[6]

But the child only begins to develop a sense of gender at about eighteen months, and then only superficially. Shortly before eighteen months, children can tell men and women, boys and girls apart, even in photos, but mainly on the basis of external appearance, such as length of hair or clothing. At about eighteen months the miracle of speech occurs, and the child starts to learn names of things, and then names of classes of things. It starts to learn the names of body parts, including its own genitalia. It becomes aware that it belongs to a certain class of people—boys or girls.

By the age of three, 65-75 percent of children correctly identify themselves as a boy or girl, but most do not at age two and a half. Kohlberg[7] observed a boy of two and a half years who went round the family circle saying "I'm boy," "Daddy boy," "Mommy boy," "Joey [a brother] boy." After correction he dropped his mother from the list, but still became confused about the gender of those outside the family. Kindergarten age children already know from pictures of toys what a boy would like to play with and what a girl would. They can also identify the sex of dolls correctly. They will not be persuaded to change these opinions, even with the offer of a reward! But they are still not clear what male or female really is, and categories and their properties are still very fluid and fuzzy at ages three to six. Before the age of six, children tend to believe in a form of magic; they believe a car could change into a truck under the right circumstances, or a boy into a girl. The famous psychologist Piaget and his followers demonstrated this. He found most four year olds thought a girl could be a boy if she changed into boy clothes, cut her hair like a boy, and played boy games. Another example is given by Kohlberg:

"The following comments were made by Jimmy, just turning four, to his four and a half year old friend Johnny:

Johnny: I'm going to be an airplane builder when I grow up.

Jimmy: When I grow up, I'll be a Mommy.

Johnny: No, you can't be a Mommy. You have to be a Daddy.

Jimmy: No, I'm going to be a Mommy.

Johnny: No, you're not a girl, you can't be a Mommy.

Jimmy: Yes I can."[7]

By the age of four or five, children tend to make distinctions between adult males and females on the basis of strength or size, and boys in particular attach great significance to these qualities. They think that social power derives from physical power, which in turn comes from physical size. "Children agree earliest and most completely that fathers are bigger and stronger than mothers, next, that they are smarter than mothers, and (by six and beyond) that they have social power and are the boss of the family." Sex roles are stereotyped on the basis of size, strength, and power at that stage; almost all of a group of sixteen four to five year old American children believed only males were policemen, soldiers, firemen, or robbers—categories involving danger and aggression. By the age of five, 97 percent of children know their gender is fixed and they cannot choose to be either a mommy or a daddy. By the age of six or seven, most are certain a girl cannot become a boy regardless of what she wears. By that age they all believe boys fight more than girls. Why? "Because girls get hurt more easily than boys." The categories and the belief about the categories have become fixed. But they are not aware of gender difference as genital difference until about five to seven, even when extensively enlightened by parents. They also have considerable difficulty accepting that the differences are natural and normal. They think that the genitalia of the opposite sex are "funny" or "wrong," or have been cut off, or that perhaps one will grow more like the other.

Even though adult females are seen as less powerful and competent than males, female stereotypes are still powerful enough to make femininity attractive to young girls. The mother or female teacher is more competent and feminine than the young girl. Femininity is associated with "niceness," nurture and helpfulness, and superior attractiveness for children aged six to seven. Girls continue to prefer feminine objects and activities at all ages.

Parent-Child Relationships

Psychologists differ over details of the process, but all concede the importance of attachment to the parent of the same sex (or a surrogate), the start of a dependent relationship, and imitation and modeling off that parent for the formation of a sense of gender identity. The child identifies with what is masculine or feminine in the parent of the same sex and absorbs it in a kind of daily osmosis. In identifying with his father ("I am like Daddy"), the boy makes the shift away from his mother that is essential for development of a masculine personality. For this shift to occur, the father needs to be an attractive and "salient" figure to the child: present, involved, warm, interested. Nicolosi[8] says a father needs to be dominant and nurturing to be "salient". Paternal warmth—as perceived by the child or by the mother—has consistently been linked to a boy's willingness to identify with his father and masculinity of preferences.[7] A "bad" father who creates conflict is worse for the boy's masculinity than no father at all. An emotionally warm and involved father also has an affirming effect on a girl's developing gender identity as she models her mother and peers.

Psychologists agree that the girl identifies primarily with her mother throughout childhood. By age four, she is clearly identifying with her mother more than her father. Although her identification with her father increases over the years four to nine, it has the effect of reinforcing her feminine values and feminine identification rather than weakening them. The same effect of mother identification does not occur nearly as strongly for boys. The little girl tends to stay near her mother and is encouraged to imitate her and do "mother" things. She learns and copies dress, appearance, and behavior. The boy has a more difficult task than the girl, who retains her primary attachment to her mother. He has to separate himself from his mother and learn to imitate his father. This is quite a conceptual leap, and it is no surprise that boys are significantly slower to mature socially than girls. The girl also separates from her mother, but later and in a much more subtle way. Imitations of mother and father are well advanced by age three.

Peer Group Relationships

By ages three and four, boys are showing clear preferences for boy-type activities, toys, and boy friends rather than girl friends, preferences that remain stable or increase with age. For girls, the choice of girl-type activities and toys, and girls as preferred friends, is well established by the same ages, but does not increase. When Koch observed pre-school children, he found 80-90 percent of friends were of the same sex. It seems quite reasonable, comments Kohlberg, to attribute the same-sex preference of both boys and girls aged three to five to the child's need to maintain its gender identity. Similarity leads to affiliation—boys and girls play with their own sex because they are like them.

So, by age three, boys and girls are already playing in different ways, and each group is quite distinct. Boys can become quite contemptuous of girls. When three-and-a-half-year old Joey was asked if he wanted any girls at his birthday party, he said, "No, I hate girls, girls are icky!"—a judgment partly informed by his natural growth, partly by his slightly older brother.[7]

Numerous studies show that boys play in a way which already echoes adult male society: games emphasizing competition and rules and winners and losers. Disputes about rules, or indeed about anything, are common, and a hierarchy is established in which each boy knows his (temporary) place. Boys tend to try to order each other about, reflecting their place in the hierarchy. Boys increasingly define their masculinity in terms of competitive achievement and acceptance in male groups. Girls, on the other hand, value relationships, and, if a game starts to cause disputes, it is usually abandoned. Girls want relationships, whereas boys want to be independent. Girls want to work together in an egalitarian sort of way and try to reach consensus by suggestion rather than orders.

By the age of eight, roughly 85 percent of both sexes believe their own sex is best. Boys who cross the line are mercilessly teased. "No-girls-allowed" activities are common to boys, in the attempt, some psychologists believe, by the boy to consolidate his gender identity following the shift in identification to his father. Boys listen increasingly to what their associates want and believe, rather than to their parents, imbibing the sense of what is acceptably masculine from each other. As LaTorre says, the sexual orientation "soaks in from the outside."[6] A similar process happens for girls. The peer group has a similar role to that of the same-sex parent. Mixing mainly with their own sex strengthens a child's sense of being male or female, and the differences deepen.

As the differences increase, a natural curiosity develops about the other group, and this leads in a significant minority of cases to sexual investigation and experimentation; by the age of seven and eight more than one half of boys have been sexually exploratory with other boys and more than half with girls, usually without the knowledge of their parents. Only about half the girls were involved in pre-pubertal "sex play" of any kind. In more than two thirds of cases, the experimentation took place only once or twice, suggesting curiosity rather than attraction.[9, 10] There are stirrings of sexual fantasy in a faint pre-echo of puberty. Boys, in particular, become more interested in the sexual nature of female adults. Most of this appears to be attraction of opposites rather than hormonally driven.

One recent piece of scientific research adds an interesting perspective to parental and peer influences on later sexual behavior. Kendrick and colleagues at the Babraham Institute in Cambridge allowed ten ewes to raise goats from birth and ten nanny goats to raise lambs from birth. The fostered kids and lambs grew up in mixed flocks of sheep and goats but the kids fraternized mainly with lambs and adopted their play and grooming habits, and the lambs fraternized mainly with kids. Once mature they ignored their own species and tried to mate 90% of the time with the foster mother species.[11] They kept this up every day during an observation period of three years, and even after years of mixing with their own species, the males did not revert (but females did). If the sexuality of these lower animals was so influenced by learning, human sexuality will be more so.

Puberty

The next milestone in heterosexual development is puberty. In boys, the body is flooded with the male hormone, testosterone; in girls, the female hormones, estrogen and progesterone. In boys, the voice deepens, the genitals enlarge, and body hair thickens; in girls, breasts develop and menstruation begins. Both become aware of themselves as sexual creatures. Boys experience their first erotic arousal at about age thirteen, and romantic fantasy begins in girls. In heterosexuality, this new sensation is expressed toward the opposite sex. But puberty does not create a sex drive that overrides existing sexual orientations, preferences, attractions, and emotional attachments. The hormonal surge only eroticizes the psychological orientation that already exists. In people with a developing heterosexual orientation, sexual desire is expressed toward the opposite sex.

Even in intersexes, the pubertal surge usually expresses itself according to the gender of upbringing. Hermaphrodites who have male gonads are often raised as girls because of their ambiguous external genitalia as

infants, but at puberty they are flooded with male hormones and have erotic dreams (in a way which a young
woman is much less likely to), the equivalent of the male
"wet dreams," but the imagery in their dreams is typical
of young women's dreams, not young men's.[12]

Sexual orientation is unsteady at the start. In early
adolescence, deep emotional involvements with the opposite sex are quite rare, and there is usually a "superficial game-like quality to heterosexual interaction. . . . It
is almost like the play behavior of the child."[6] Although
they are also associating strongly with their same-sex
peers, and confirming their own gender, adolescents often
doubt their own masculinity or femininity at this stage.
Same sex sexual experimentation is quite high in adolescent boys; 12 percent reach orgasm with another person
of the same sex, but usually only once or twice.[10]

Falling In Love

"Falling in love" rather than childish 'crushes' is another stage in the process of becoming fully heterosexual,
one that doesn't appear to be related to puberty, puberty being hormonal, and falling in love social. Researchers know of some cases of girls falling in love before
age twelve, but no cases of boys doing so. Even those
children who are precociously sexually mature at very
early ages—such as eight—do not fall in love, although
many of them have definite heterosexual fantasy, or
dreams leading to orgasm, and may masturbate. In one
case reported in 1932, a boy who became sexually mature before the age of four was reported to have made
"obvious and distressing sexual advances to adult women
with whom he was left alone." But he did not fall in
love.[12] Falling in love can happen in some cases without
puberty, and indeed even without any gonads, but only
past a minimum age.[12] Falling in love doesn't seem to be
biologically driven; rather, it seems to require a certain
age and stage of social development.

In the romantic West, an ocean of ink has been used up in the description of this most mysterious of sensations, but "falling in love" is not really very mysterious. A lot is now known about why people in the West are attracted to each other. In his book *Families and How to Survive Them,*[13] Robin Skynner, a family therapist, boils attraction down to three things: social pressures (class, religion, and money), conscious personal reasons like good looks and shared interests, and unconscious attractions—commonly called 'chemistry'. To demonstrate how chemistry works, Skynner breaks his new classes up into groups while they are still strangers to each other and asks each person to choose "another person from the group who either makes them think of someone in their family or gives them the feeling that they would have filled a 'gap' in their family." No one is allowed to speak during the exercise. When they have found each other they are encouraged to see if they can find out why they chose each other, and to talk about their family backgrounds. Then each couple chooses another couple, making foursomes, and then each foursome forms itself into a family of some kind, agreeing with each other about roles. In each case, Skynner reports, people choose others whose families have functioned in very similar ways to their own—for example, difficulty in showing affection, incestuous relationships, absentee fathers, or obligatory cheerfulness. In this group exercise, there are always people who are not chosen. The first time Skynner tried the exercise, this group of leftovers found they had all been fostered, adopted, or brought up in children's homes. Although Skynner concedes his trainees are deliberately looking for someone making them think of their families, he says we are unconsciously attracted to certain kinds of people in a way that somehow mirrors the way we learned to relate in our families. In other words, to a significant extent our responses when we "fall in love" have been unconsciously learned. They are not always healthy.

But in many non-western cultures, marriages are arranged, and people fall in love after they are married. That's the way the culture does it, and if the arrangement is a good one, socially and economically, and there is mutual consideration, love usually follows.

A recent study[14] of 445 pairs of twins, most of them identical, found no genetic contribution to the way "people make emotional attachments to each other." Rather, the study found that spouses were more like their partners in "love attitudes" than twins were to each other.

If heterosexuality were genetic, one would expect an indiscriminate attraction to the opposite sex across the board. But (excluding incest, which falls in a different category) this is not the case. Young men do not want to marry their sisters, unless they have been separated from them during their upbringing.[9] Studies in Israeli kibbutzim, in which unrelated children are raised together from a very early age while parents work, show they do not find each other erotically interesting in adolescence, though there are no restrictions on romantic involvement between kibbutzniks. In one study, all the young people without exception married outside the group they had grown up with.[12]

A recent study by Bem[15] argues that what is "exotic becomes erotic". In other words, a large part of what drives sexual attraction is the mystery of the other sex which has developed separately for years in childhood.

Cultural Conditioning

Sexual attraction and behavior also depend on the conventions of a particular culture. In *Wild Swans,*[16] an account of three generations of women in a Chinese family, Jung Chang writes of the custom of foot-binding.

"My grandmother was a beauty . . . but her greatest assets were her bound feet, called in Chinese . . . 'three inch golden lilies.' " Not only was the sight of women hobbling on tiny feet considered erotic, men would also get excited playing with bound feet, which were always hidden in embroidered silk shoes.

When Jung Chang's great grandfather was seeking a suitor for his daughter, he planned the first meeting so that this daughter's "tiny feet" would be seen to advantage in their "embroidered satin shoes."

The custom has clear cultural origins. It began about a thousand years earlier when a Chinese emperor bound the feet of his concubines to stop them from running away. But they became erotic symbols—in spite of the fact that bones were broken and deformed in the binding process and that the dead skin stank when the bandages were removed.

The attraction of Victorian men to women's ankles was another "cultural" erotic response. So is the reaction of males in some Moslem cultures to a naked female arm.

It is common for members of one culture to not be particularly erotically attracted to members of another, at least initially. It takes time to appreciate the social conventions of what is erotic in a particular culture and how well a person fulfils them.

Highly Individual Factors

People also develop their sexual orientation and preferences through chance incidents, random circumstances unique to the individual that are in some way associated with sexual arousal. Once the behavior starts it tends to be repeated, and gradually become habitual.

According to Gebhard of the Kinsey Institute, unusual behaviors and preferences can often be traced back to one-off incidents of this nature. He gives two examples. A young teenage boy experienced strong sexual arousal when he was wrestling with an older girl who was stronger than he was and on top of him. He later developed an attraction to large, muscular, dominant females, tried to include wrestling in love play, and became a bit masochistic. In another case, a boy broke his arm, which,

because of the circumstances, had to be set without an-
esthetic. It was extremely painful. While this was being
done the doctor's nurse clasped him close to comfort
him. He became sexually aroused and later developed a
fetish for brunette hair styles the same as the nurse's.
His sexual behavior also became somewhat
sadomasochistic. Gebhard places considerable emphasis
on the role of chance circumstances in the development
of sexuality. He comments about data "which show to an
almost frightening degree the power of chance operat-
ing through variables in the immediate situation."[17]

Habit Formation and Addiction

According to Gebhard, any kind of heterosexual activity started soon after puberty almost invariably continues from then on. In other words, what we start doing we
tend to keep on doing unless the negative consequences
outweigh the perceived benefits. We form a habit. If the
habit becomes a way of relieving emotional pain, it can
become addictive.

Summary

No-one appears to be born heterosexual. Rather,
heterosexual attraction appears to be learned, developing over a period of time in response to certain environmental factors, in particular:
• Good maternal nurture from the earliest stages
and through the first few years: nursing, feeding, loving,
touching, talking, closeness, eye contact, and care of physical needs. Where this is present the first stage of heterosexual development takes place: the child responds and
attaches to the caregiver. Without it, the child's incentive
to identify and imitate is weak and social development
suffers. If the early deprivation has been severe and long-
term, we seem to end up with people who lack an essential element of sexual orientation—the ability to experience or show affection either to the opposite sex or to
the same sex.

• Identification with and imitation of the parent of the same sex (or other close same-sex models).

• Acceptance by and identification with same-sex peer groups.

• Identification in a boy with what is culturally "masculine" and in a girl with what is culturally "feminine" (gender conformity).

• The day-in-day-out treatment of boys and girls, as boys or girls respectively. (The slowly developing awareness of gender in a boy or girl suggests that gender identity is not programmed in from day one, but is learned; slowly acquired in complex ways from the social environment.)

• The biologically-programmed hormonal rush of puberty. This might be expected to be the strongest determining factor in sexual orientation, but puberty only adds sexual drive to whatever prevailing psychological gender identity is already present. That is, it reinforces existing gender orientation but doesn't change it.

• Falling in love. This appears to be unrelated to genes or puberty; it is something environmentally conditioned that requires a minimum chronological and social age.

• Culturally prescribed sexual behaviors, like arousal over women's bound feet.

• Personal sexual preferences and behaviors that can be traced back to early sexual arousal in unique circumstances.

If anything was going to be programmed into the genetic code, you would think heterosexuality would be. The urge to survive and reproduce ought to be one of the most basic in the species. But heterosexuality seems to be a psycho-social learning process spread over many years.

Homosexuality

If heterosexuality is learned, what about homosexuality?

Relationships with Parents and Peer Groups

The psychological literature on homosexuality clearly reveals breakdowns in learning processes critical to the development of heterosexuality. Rather than bonding and identifying with same-sex parents, imitating and role-modeling, numerous studies of homosexuals show early breaches, negative relationships, and resistance to identification and modeling. One comprehensive study of homosexuality[18] found 84 percent of homosexual men said their fathers were indifferent and uninvolved compared with 10 percent of heterosexual men, and that only 10 percent of homosexual men identified with their fathers in childhood, compared with two thirds of heterosexual men.

Rather than boys playing with boys and girls with girls, studies show pre-homosexual children have few friends of the same sex and are rejected by same-sex peer groups. They show boys who played with girls, didn't like male sports, and wanted to be around women more than men. In a review of the literature,[8] van den Aardweg says poor relationships with peer groups are even more common in the backgrounds of male homosexuals than poor relationships with fathers.

Numerous empirical studies have shown that homosexual women have poorer relationships with their mothers than heterosexual women.[19] Saghir and Robins[18] found only 23 percent of homosexual women reported positive relationships with their mothers and identification with them, compared with 85 percent of heterosexual women.

Bell et al.[19] comment that, in both boys and girls, a negative relationship with the same-sex parent reduces the desire to identify with that parent. Children with reduced identification are more likely to develop "gender non-conformity" ("sissiness" in boys and "tomboyism" in girls; the sense of feeling "different" from their peers). This is what we find in male and female homosexuality. A boy who has not bonded well with his father and has only a weak identification with him is not developing a sense of masculine identity. Nicolosi remarks that "the masculine qualities conveyed in the healthy father-son relationship are confidence and independence, assertiveness and a sense of personal power."[8] Without these attributes, he will not fit well into childhood male peer groups. Male homosexual clients characteristically say they were rejected by childhood male peer groups because they were "weak, unmasculine, unacceptable." That's when the name-calling starts—"sissy," "girl." Saghir and Robins found 67 percent of homosexuals were called sissy or effeminate by others, (compared with three percent of heterosexual men), and that 79 percent of these men in childhood and early adolescence had no male friends, played mostly with girls, and rarely or never played sports.[18]

A similar pattern is seen in lesbianism. Young girls resistant to mother identification and modeling do not fit well into female peer groups. In Saghir and Robins' group, 70 percent of homosexual women were "tomboys" as children, compared with 16 percent of heterosexual women. They had no girl playmates (unlike pre-heterosexual girls), played mostly with boys, and were active in team sports. Most rejected playing with dolls and showed no interest in domestic role-modeling. Sixty three percent wished they were boys or men, compared with only seven percent of heterosexual women. The attitude persists into adulthood. One of the two findings that differentiated lesbian women from heterosexual women was the feeling in lesbian women that they were less feminine and more masculine. "They express disinterest in feminine accessories and fashion, prefer 'sporty' and tailored clothes, and shun make-up and hairdos. They see their social and domestic roles as being incompatible with those of other women. They behave more competitively and are oriented toward career and accomplishments with little interest in raising children or in domestic pursuits."[18]

It is important to note that this effect, "childhood
gender non-conformity," is one of the strongest effects
known in the psychological literature on any gender
behavior and is an excellent predictor of later homosexuality.[15]

Sexual Activity and Sexual Abuse

Several major studies have highlighted more childhood and adolescent homosexual activity in pre-homosexual children and adolescents. Van Wyk and Geist,[9]
looking at a sample of 7669 white male and female
Americans, say both lesbians and homosexuals were more
likely to have had intense pre-pubertal sexual contact
with boys or men. They draw a link between sexual abuse
and later lesbianism, but also say that most lesbians
learned to masturbate by being masturbated by a female.
It appears that these women as growing girls had retreated from distressing male sexual contact at the same
time as they had also experienced female sexual contact.
By contrast, young pre-homosexual males appear not so
much to be in flight from female sexual contact, as to
find satisfaction in male sexual contact. Male homosexuals were more likely than heterosexual men to have been
masturbated by other men or boys, they comment, and
"once arousal to the particular type of stimulus occurs, it
tends quite rapidly to form a pattern."

Ex-gay support groups (see chapter twelve) report
that between 50 percent and 60 percent of homosexual
men coming for help have been abused sexually.[20]
Finkelhor found young men sexually abused by older
males were about four times more likely to engage in
homosexual activity as adults.[20] Nichols reports male
sexual abuse of lesbians is twice as high as in heterosexual women.[21] Gundlach and Riess[22] report a similar
figure. Ex-gay groups report high levels of male sexual
abuse (up to 85 percent) in female homosexuals who
come for help.[20] Peters and Cantrell (cited elsewhere[22])
found more than two thirds of lesbians reported being

forced into sexual experiences with males after the age of twelve, compared with only 28 percent of heterosexuals.

So sexual abuse appears to be a factor in the development of homosexuality. Ex-gay groups suggest that when a boy's relationships with father and peer group are unhappy, childhood and adolescent sexual intimacy with another man leads to a later association of sex with male interest, affection, and acceptance. One former homosexual, Michael Saia,[23] says homosexual men are not looking for sex when they have their first sexual encounter. He says they are looking for acceptance, understanding, companionship, strength, security, and a sense of completeness. Sex becomes the way to get it. "I was starved of affection," said Bob. "I didn't like the sex at first, I just wanted someone to really love me. I told myself, OK, if this is what I have to do to get the touch, I'll do it. Then it got to where I liked it. So . . . " Lesbianism, on the other hand, is primarily emotional rather than sexual. Lesbianism is a relationship in which two women's strongest emotions, affections and sexual feelings are directed toward each other.

Later studies of non-clinical groups have shown no difference in sexual abuse between heterosexual and lesbian groups. Chapman and Brannock,[24] for example, show women questioning their sexual orientation because they feel strong emotional and/or sexual bonds with women rather than because they have been sexually abused by the opposite sex. This accords with the findings of one researcher in developmental psychology, Dr. Elizabeth Moberly, whose conclusions have been widely accepted by the international ex-gay movement. Moberly[25] sees sexual abuse as a secondary contributor to homosexuality. She posits the main cause as early "defensive detachment" from the parent of the same sex that interferes critically with the identification process that produces a sense of gender in children. This breach between a child and the same sex parent (which, she says, could happen for any number of reasons, and is as often a result of childhood misperception of parents' actions as parental neglect or abuse), structures itself into the relationship and leaves the child with a deep need for the same-sex love, affection, and gender identity that it has rejected or which has not been provided. Difficulties in attachment and identification lead to feelings of alienation in same sex peer groups and from then on homosexual development follows a fairly predictable course: a deep need for same sex affection, affirmation, acceptance, and sense of gender identity; masturbation and/or fantasy around a certain admired same sex figure; a sexual encounter; the beginning of habitual responses; self-identification as homosexual; "coming out;" finding partners; the homosexual lifestyle; civil rights. Most people with homo-emotional needs and homosexual responses, however, do not "come out" to friends and family or live a visibly homosexual or activist life-style.

In one of the largest studies of a homosexual population, Bell, et al., said homosexuality could not be traced back to "a single psychological or social root."[19] However, they gave the highest values to a constellation of factors: negative relationship with the parent of the same sex, "childhood gender non conformity," and adolescent homosexual arousal and activity.

So, if heterosexuality results from a learning process that involves relationships with parents and peer groups, puberty, sexual encounters, highly individual experiences, and repeated behaviors, so does homosexuality.

If homosexuality were genetically predestined, one would not expect a slow development of the condition, but a universal awareness of same-sex attraction from earliest years. However, Dr. Dean Hamer, looking at eighty men living openly as homosexuals, found half did not experience same-sex attraction until the ages of ten to seventeen years.[26] Self-identification as homosexual typically came about five years later. For actively homosexual men who are married, somewhere between a third and two thirds of them concluded they were homosexual only after they married.[27, 28]

No Sexual Orientation

A total lack of sexual orientation is common but mostly temporary, caused by illness, depression, marital conflict or negative sexual experiences. In this state called anhedonia, the light has gone from all pleasures, not just sexual ones. The Kinsey Institute in 1970 found about 10 percent of the adult population (8.9 percent of men, 11.8 percent of women) saw no prospect of sexual enjoyment with either sex.[10] A 1980 survey of forty year old women found one third never had spontaneous libido.[29] A 1987 survey of British women aged thirty-five to thirty-nine found 17 percent had seriously diminished libido.[29] In contrast some bisexuals seek heterosexual partners except when tired or depressed when they seek homosexual ones. These examples show the malleability of sexual orientation.

A few people appear never to have learnt a sexual orientation. Leiblum says the patients often show "a chronic lifelong lack of sexual interest. . . . Often we are unable to identify evidence of psychic inhibition of libido in such individuals but rather seem to be dealing with a permanent state of 'asexuality.' Sexual stirrings or urges seem not to occur instead of being blocked or repressed."[29] One researcher[30] described the unusual situation of a married couple with complete lack of sexual interest, who had known each other since childhood and discovered their common indifference. They appear to have married for companionship. When interviewed, they had lived together twenty years and slept in each other's arms, but there was no genital contact at all. There was no physical abnormality. They were quite content. This may not be a complete lack of sexual orientation, but it had no erotic expression.

Conclusion

We all tend to take our heterosexuality for granted—
as if it just happens. But it seems to develop slowly and
steadily over years—about two decades—through clearly
defined and documented stages. There are different
schools of psychology and different theories, but the psychologists are in broad agreement about the general
stages of heterosexual development and unanimous about
one thing: heterosexual orientation is not genetically
determined. They will say it is overwhelmingly learned—
the result of response to the environment. Most will also
say genetics has a part to play, but only a very minor
one. Homosexuals frequently show a breakdown in several of the developmental stages leading to heterosexuality, particularly attachment to and gender identification with the same sex parent and adequate connection
with same sex peers, leading to needs for same sex affection and affirmation that become eroticized. Once the
pattern of sexual gratification of these needs starts, a
habit begins, becomes ingrained, and then often addictive because of the underlying emotional deficits. Rates
of male sexual abuse are higher in homosexuals and
lesbians than in heterosexuals. If heterosexuality is
learned, then homosexuality is, too.

So, what role might genetics play in homosexuality?
Probably about the same role it plays in the pregnancy
of a fifteen year old girl. You could argue that if she is
born with the combination of genes that make her attractive in her culture (and therefore subject to more
sexual pressure from interested males than she would be
if she were ugly), that she is genetically predisposed to
become pregnant at age fifteen. In homosexuality, it
would seem that any biological trait that adds to a person's
sense of "gender non-conformity" (one of the strongest
predictors of later homosexuality) could be said to genetically pre-dispose him or her to a homosexual orientation.

But did your genes make you heterosexual or homosexual? No, it seems you learned it over many years.

Notes

1. Schwartz, M.F., Money, J., Robinson, K., "Biosocial perspectives on the development of the proceptive, acceptive and conceptive phases of eroticism," *Journal of Sex and Marital Therapy* (1981), 7:243-255.

2. Langmeier, J., Matejcek, Z., *Psychological Deprivation in Childhood* (New York: John Wiley and Sons, 1978).

3. Nielson, G., Young, D., Latham, S., "Multiply acting out adolescents-developmental correlates and response to secure treatment," *International Journal of Offender Therapy and Comparative Criminology* (1982), 26:195-206.

4. Deutsch, H., "Absence of grief," *Psychoanalytical Quarterly* (1937), 6:12-22.

5. Rutter, M., *Maternal Deprivation Reassessed* (U.K.: Penguin Books, Harmondsworth, Middlesex, 1981).

6. LaTorre, R.A., *Sexual Identity* (Chicago: Nelson-Hall Inc., 1979).

7. Kohlberg, L., "A cognitive-developmental analysis." In *The Development of Sex Differences* edited by E.E. Macoby (Stanford, CA: Stanford University Press, 1966), 82-173.

8. Nicolosi, J., *Reparative Therapy of Male Homosexuality* (Northvale, NJ: Jason Aronson, Inc., 1991).

9. Van Wyk, P.H., Geist, C.S., "Psychosocial development of heterosexual, bisexual and homosexual behavior," *Archives of Sexual Behavior* (1984): 13:505-544.

10. Klassen, A.D., Williams, C.J., Levitt, E.E., *Sex and Morality in the U.S.* (Connecticut: Wesleyan University Press, 1989).

Neil and Briar Whitehead

11. Kendrick, K.M., Hinton, M.R., Atkins, K., Haupt, M.A., Skinner, J.D., "Mothers Determine Sexual Preferences," *Nature* (1998), 395:229-230.

12. Money, J., Ehrhardt, A.A., *Man & Woman, Boy & Girl* (Baltimore, MD: The Johns Hopkins University Press, 1972).

13. Skynner, R., Cleese, J.O., *Families, and How To Survive Them* (Publication city not cited, Mandarin-Reed Int., 1983).

14. Mestel, R., "Love is blind. . . . to genes," *New Scientist* (10 September 1994): 143:5.

15. Bem, D.J., "Exotic becomes erotic: a developmental theory of sexual orientation," *Psychological Review* 103 (1996), 320-335.

16. Chang, J., *Wild Swans* (Flamingo, London: Wild Swans, 1993).

17. Gebhard, P.H., "Situational factors affecting human sexual behavior." In *Sex and Behavior* edited by F.A. Beach (New York: John Wiley and Sons, 1965), 483-495.

18. Saghir, M.T., Robins, E., *Male and Female Homosexuality, A Comprehensive Investigation* (Baltimore, MD: Williams and Wilkins, 1973).

19. Bell, A.P., Weinberg, M.S., Hammersmith, S.K., *Sexual Preference: Its Development In Men and Women* (Bloomington, IN: Indiana University Press, 1981).

20. Davies, B., Rentzel, L., *Coming Out Of Homosexuality* (Downers Grove, IL: InterVarsity Press, 1993).

21. Nichols, M., "Low sexual desire in lesbian couples." In *Sexual Desire Disorders* edited by S.R. Leiblum and R.C. Rosen (New York: The Guilford Press, 1988), 387-412.

22. Gundlach, R.H., Riess, B.F., "Birth order and sex of siblings in a sample of lesbians and non lesbians," *Psychological Reports* (1967), 20:61-63.

23. Saia, M., *Counselling the Homosexual* (Minneapolis, MN: Bethany House, 1988).

24. Chapman, B.E., Brannock, J.C., "Proposed model of lesbian identity development: an empirical examination," *Journal of Homosexuality* (1987), 14:69-80.

25. Moberly, E.R., *Homosexuality, A New Christian Ethic* (Cambridge: James Clarke & Co., 1983).

26. Hamer, D.H., Hu, S., Magnuson, V.L., Hu, N., Pattatucci, AML. "A linkage between DNA markers on the X-chromosome and male sexual orientation," *Science* (1993), 261:321-327.

27. Ross, M.W., *The Married Homosexual Man* (London: Routledge & Kegan Paul, 1983).

28. Wolf, T.J., "Marriages of bisexual men," *Journal of Homosexuality* (1985), 11:135-148.

29. Leiblum, S.R., Rosen, R.C., "Introduction." In *Sexual Desire Disorders* edited by S.R. Lieblum and R.C. Rosen (New York: The Guilford Press, 1988), 1-17.

30. Zilbergeld, B., Hammond, D.C., The use of hypnosis in treating desire disorders. In: (Eds., Leiblum, S.R., Rosen, R.C.) *Sexual Desire Disorders* (New York: The Guilford Press, 1988), 192-225.

Chapter Four

How Far Do Our Instincts Control Us?

People will sometimes argue that if a behavior isn't genetic, it is so deeply part of them it might as well be. They usually mean that the behavior is long-term, thoroughly embedded, and seems to be quite resistant to efforts to change it. If people wanted to argue that homosexuality was akin to a powerful human instinct, what might that mean?

We all have some strong instincts; if a car tries to run us over, we dodge, and faster than we dreamed we could! Survival is probably our strongest instinct, the maternal instinct could be next, and the infant's instinct to suckle, eat, and sleep is a close third. Young children have an instinctive fear of heights. In some experiments several decades ago, researchers placed strong sheet glass over a deep recess created in a level surface and let babies crawl along the sheet glass. All the babies paused in fear at the apparent edge and retreated.[1]

We have an instinctive fear of loud noises and fast movement of a dangerous object toward us: our body goes into the fight/flight reaction—we either attack or run for our lives! We have a blinking reflex when something comes near our eyes; digestive reflexes; a pain reflex—for example, instantaneous removal of a hand from a flame. Sleep seems to be a reflex when we are very tired. The contractions of childbirth are a reflex. We have a knee-jerk reaction when we're hit just below the kneecap. Even male ejaculation is a reflex—it can be triggered by an electric shock. Then there is the sneezing reflex, yawning. . . . you can add to the list.

Can We Train Our Instincts?

Waft enough dust or pepper into someone's nose, and almost everyone will sneeze. We sneeze instinctively. Or do we? It's true that we sneeze in response to the reaction between the dust and our nose, but there is a pause during which we can stop or go on. A finger hard under the nose may stop a sneeze; looking at bright light may encourage it; doctors can stop labor contractions with drugs; we can stifle a yawn. Some reflexes can be trained, and trained surprisingly far. It is natural to blink when something is put in your eye, but if you wear contact lenses you can learn to control that and (usually) not blink until the lens is in the eye.

We can train many of our most basic instincts. We can train ourselves to ignore hunger pangs, and fast for religious or other reasons. When we have gone without food for a few days, we are not taken over by reflexes which force us to drop everything and concentrate all our attentions on getting food—indeed, after a few days the hunger pangs tend to disappear altogether and reappear only after the traditional forty days fast, when the body is at its last extremity. Considering we'll die quite soon if we don't eat, it's amazing how weak the influence of hunger on behavior is.

Similarly, although we will die or go mad if deprived of sleep for weeks, the sleep reflex is not overwhelming. We can keep ourselves awake for an all-night event.

As a baby grows, it slowly learns to lose its fear of heights, at least enough to climb trees, hills, and in extreme cases mountains and overhanging rock faces. The rock climber may even enjoy the tension and fear! Blondin walking a tightrope over the Niagara Falls; Houdini the escape artist bound in chains, locked in a casket and dropped underwater; both had brought their survival instincts under control and revelled in the risk. Soldiers trained in mock battle conditions, senses assaulted by the loud shock of nearby explosions, learn to overcome their fear of death and obey orders. On the real battle-field their training holds up—they fight rather than fly. So even the fear of death can be controlled.

Maternal Instinct

The mothering instinct is among the most powerful instincts. In the animal kingdom, timid ewes will charge humans and dogs if their lambs are threatened. Most mothers will protect their young. You would expect the mothering instinct in man to be more deeply pro-grammed than in any species, because the newborn baby is unusually defenseless at birth. Its brain is so undevel-oped that it will die if it is not mothered for the first few years. Mothers are equipped to conceive, carry, and suckle their young. They appear to be the natural nurturers.

Fathers don't appear to have the same instinct to nurture. Surveys usually show that they spend only about one third of the time with their children that mothers do.[2] Are human males biologically programmed to be poor nurturers, much more instinctively geared to fight aggressively outside the home to provide food for their families? Are we like the rats? The female rat constantly attentive to her young, licking, feeding, and guarding them, and looking after the nest structure; the male rat a menace, aggressively biting, and even eating young rats! Is this evidence for strong instinctive differences between male and female?

If that is the case, then it can certainly be repro-grammed. In an unusual experiment, scientist Jay Rosenblatt[3] took several-day-old rats and put them in with virgin females. The females showed no mothering instincts and of course could not nurse the pups, so the pups tended to languish. Rosenblatt replaced the pups each day, and by the sixth day there was an enormous change in the behavior of the virgin females. They began to look after the pups, licking them, retrieving them, and even more astonishingly, lying down as though trying to nurse them. Even though they were not primed by the hormonal changes of pregnancy, the presence of the pups alone was sufficient to trigger the maternal behavior.

Rosenblatt tried exactly the same thing with adult male rats. After six days, the males started behaving just like the virgin females: licking the pups, retrieving them when they strayed, and even lying down as though trying to nurse them! In other words, maternal "instincts" were evoked by the presence of the pups in male rats, sometimes known to eat their infant offspring.

In rhesus monkeys the typical indifference of male monkeys towards infants can be broken down to the extent that they will show "maternalistic feelings as tender and solicitous as any shown by a rhesus mother" to any infant who needs care.[3]

There is a celebrated instance in which a wild bitch died five weeks after giving birth, and the remaining five adult male dogs raised the nine pups themselves.[3] In about 40 percent of primates, males care for the young. Sometimes they snatch the infant from the mother apparently for the sheer pleasure of carrying it about. Among the marmoset and tamarin monkeys, it is hard to say which is the primary caregiver.

Obviously, male behavior is not firmly and instinctively imprinted in lower animals. It can be radically changed. The old rule applies: if lower animals, whose behavior is much more biologically programmed than ours, can retrain natural instincts, then human beings can to a much greater degree. The modern woman who insists that men are quite capable of mothering and nurturing children appears to have science on her side; fathers are certainly able to increase the quality time they already spend with their children.[4] Certainly "househusbands" have brought up very young children. With glass bottles and rubber teats, a father can even nurse a child! There have even been a few rare cases of older men who (probably through some hormonal disturbance) were able to breast-feed young children. Similar hormonally disturbed cases, some induced by hormone treatment to fight tumors, are reported reasonably frequently.[5]

Nor is maternal behavior an over-riding instinct in human females. Some human mothers abandon their babies at birth. Hundreds of thousands of babies are aborted each year. Some women are poor mothers; some men make good ones. It seems the mothering instinct can be developed or neglected in a woman, and evoked in a man.

Sexuality

The urge to reproduce—to ensure the survival of the species—is a powerful instinct. But, like the survival instinct and the maternal instinct, it is not an overwhelming reflex. In fact, it can be controlled with training, as many in religious orders know. As we mentioned in chapter three, a significant minority (about 10 percent) of the general population has no wish to reproduce at all. So the urge to perpetuate the species is obviously not an over-riding drive.

Actually, our sexual instincts often have to be rather vigorously prodded before they'll move into the driver's seat. The ejaculation reflex only takes over when a certain threshold of stimulation is passed, and usually quite a bit of stimulation is needed. We might not want to stop, but we can. Our instincts do not control us. The Bible says, "Blessed is the man who controls his spirit [the drives which move him in various ways]. He is better than the man who captures a castle" (Proverbs 16:32). What makes our sexuality appear so powerful is all the training it gets. We are encouraged to express the sexual side of our natures. So, even though our urge or need for sexual expression might end up feeling irresistible, it's really no more than an over-developed instinct, demand-fed hundreds of times for decades.

Homosexuality

Homosexuals cannot reproduce, so homosexual activity cannot be considered an instinct to perpetuate the species. If it could be called an instinct, it is no less malleable than any other of the powerful instincts that man experiences, which, we have seen, are subject to a huge degree to man's will and other environmental influences.

Addiction

Addiction is not an instinct, but can become something very close to an instinct. The surfaces of body cells are chemically configured in such a way that they resemble a lock waiting for the right key to turn in it. The chemistry of certain drugs is like the key that turns perfectly in the receptors of cells in certain organs of the body, and, after a while, the reaction becomes a part of the cells' life, creating a chemical dependency which the body feels as a need. If pleasurable sensations accompany the process and this "hooks" into some way of relieving emotional pain, then an addictive cycle begins, minimal at the start but increasing in strength until it seems almost impossible to control. Is addictive behavior an uncontrollable compulsion? Has the cell physiology made us do it? No, we helped it hundreds of times. But it's possible to reverse the process and rediscover the old normalcy (or find a new one).

Conclusion

We can learn to bring our instincts under control, or we can allow our instincts to control us. Instincts develop because they are fed. No behavior takes us over without years of encouragement. If we have spent all our lives cultivating a certain behavior by thousands of repeated actions and responses, then it will eventually seem like a powerful urge—so powerful that it seems irresistible, or even genetically programmed. But nothing is unchangeable. If we can lose our fear of death with training, and even enjoy the risks, if fathers can become "mothers," then sexual reflexes can also be trained. It may take a few years to reverse the training we have given them, but it can be done.

We are created to be voluntary animals, not involuntary ones. On these grounds alone, it makes no sense at all to maintain we are doing something we just can't help doing. Somehow, we have trained ourselves into the habit. Though not without difficulty, we can just as effectively train ourselves out of it, if we really want to. But we will need the help of others and of God.

Homosexuality, if some want to call it an instinct, is no different from any other instinct.

Notes

1. Gibson, E.J., Walk, R.D., "The Visual Cliff," *Scientific American* (April 1960): 64-71.

2. Weiss, D.E., *The Great Divide* (New York: Poseidon Press, 1991).

3. Shaw, E., Darling, J., "Maternalism—The Fathering of a Myth," *New Scientist* (14 February 1985): 10-13.

4. Mackey, W.C., "A cross cultural perspective on perceptions of paternalistic deficiencies in the United States, The myth of the derelict Daddy," *Sex Roles* (1985): 122:509-533.

5. Hayashi, T., Taki, Y., Ikai, K., Hiura, M., Kiriyama, T., "Hormonal environment following treatment with a small dose of estrogen—small dose of estrogen alone and in combination with an antiandrogen." *Hinyokika Kiyo* (1987): 33:1035-1042.

Chapter Five

What Produces the Sexual Identity of Intersexes?

A study of people with ambiguous genitalia gives unusual endorsement to the role of the environment and upbringing in shaping human sexuality. The majority of intersexes (people of ambiguous gender appearance) who have come to the attention of researchers have opted for the gender of upbringing (rather than their chromosomal gender) when they have been offered corrective medical intervention.

Sometimes babies are born with such ambiguous genitalia that medical staff do not know whether the child is a boy or a girl. In the past, parents instructed to raise these children in one gender or other often found them developing physically (usually with the onset of puberty) contrary to the gender of upbringing. But, when these children were given the option of corrective surgery and hormonal intervention at puberty, 90 percent of those whose cases have been researched opted for the gender in which they had been raised, rather than their biological gender, even in the face of quite contrary physical characteristics. In many cases, these children grew up to develop gender behaviors consistent with their gender of choice, rather than their biological gender. They felt attraction, experienced erotic arousal, fell in love in ways characteristic of their chosen gender, married, and raised children.

A Lesson In Biology

Almost everyone, including homosexuals and lesbians is born chromosomally female (XX) or chromosomally male (XY). When a male sperm carrying twenty-three chromosomes unites with the female ovum, also carrying twenty-three chromosomes, the fertilized egg quickly becomes a forty-six chromosome cell of twenty-three pairs, one of each pair from the father, one from the mother. All the chromosomes carry the genetic material that gives us our biological characteristics, but the twenty-third pair is the sex chromosomes, usually comprised of one X chromosome inherited from the mother and an X or Y chromosome inherited from the father. An XX combination in the fertilized egg produces a female, and an XY combination produces a male. Sometimes these standard combinations do not happen, and rare combinations result for reasons that are still not very clear to researchers. One of the X chromosomes can be "lost," leaving only a single X. These fertilized X cells still grow normally, but produce individuals who are very short (4½-5ft.) and physically female, but have no ovaries and are infertile, a condition called Turner's syndrome. Some cells end up XXX, resulting in women with a normal female body, but diminished fertility, and sometimes mental retardation. Males can be XYY, with male body type, reduced fertility, and increased height; XXY or XXXY (Klinefelter's syndrome) both cause male body type, but with unusually small penises, shrunken testes, and varying but low production of the male hormone, testosterone, so that at puberty they become only moderately masculine and have scant body hair. The percentage of homosexuals among people with Klinefelter's syndrome is about typical for the general population, but about half of those with the syndrome are uninterested in any type of sex (they are quite prone to sexual anxiety), partly due to their physical attributes. Such varied sexuality means it is not forced on them by their chromosomal pattern.[1]

There are all sorts of rare combinations of X and Y, but, in general, if people have an XY or XX combination of some kind they will develop physically as male or female respectively.[2]

Overwhelming Effects of Rearing

John Money, Anke Ehrhardt, and John and Joan Hampson, at the Johns Hopkins Medical School in Baltimore, Maryland, have spent a lifetime studying unusual sexual conditions and intersexes. What they found in the sixties about the role of upbringing in the formation of gender identity and sexual orientation led them to the conclusion that the influence of upbringing and rearing was so overwhelming that it was as if a new-born child was a blank slate, written upon only by the influence of upbringing and socialization.[3]

Andrenogenital Syndrome In Females

This condition, which affects female fetuses, is the result of a genetic defect; the adrenal glands do not produce their proper hormone, cortisone. Instead, they release a precursor product, which acts as a male hormone, an androgen. This enters the bloodstream of the female fetus too late to masculinize the internal reproductive system, which is already female, but in time to masculinize the external genitalia. The result is a chromosomal female with a uterus and two ovaries, but anything from a grossly enlarged clitoris resembling a penis with partially fused labia (resembling testicles) to a fully formed penis and empty scrotum. Because people with this condition continue to produce androgen for the rest of their lives, they must also take doses of the antidote, cortisone, to counteract it: in childhood, to stop an excessively masculine puberty which comes eight to ten years too early, but also in adulthood. Although the ovaries continue to secrete normal levels of female hormones, these are overwhelmed by the high amounts of androgen being produced by the adrenal gland.

Six Cases

Money writes about six females, all with andrenogenital syndrome,[2] whom he interviewed as teenagers and adults. They were all chromosomally XX and had typically female uterus and ovaries, but had been exposed to the male hormone androgen before birth, so their genitalia looked masculine. After puberty, four of the six opted for the sex in which they had been raised rather than their chromosomal gender. In the two other cases the parents had raised them ambiguously (neither definitely as boys or girls) because of their own confusion. One decided to be a girl, even though her body was precociously masculine, and the other to be a boy, in accordance with his precociously masculine body. These two cases showed the greatest psychological distress. Five of the cases are summarized below.

Case One: The child was raised as a boy, given cortisone to stop precocious and excessive masculinization, and, at puberty, androgen therapy. Artificial testes were implanted in the empty scrotum. The child had an unhappy homelife (his father was sick and his parents fought). He was an academic underachiever and sought semi-delinquent company, where he gained status as a rebel. The boys accepted him as one of themselves. Psychosexually, "all of his romantic feelings and approaches were towards girls," though he was nervous about attempting intercourse with an undersize penis and artificial testes.

Case Two: Born with a small phallus and empty scrotum, she was designated a boy and given cortisone each day. However, because "he" had ovaries secreting the female hormone estrogen, he began (to his disgust!) to develop breasts at eleven. At twelve the correct chromosomal sex was diagnosed, but the boy decided against sex reassignment. Said the mother, "He has a sister and they are completely different. He does not think like a girl and he does not have the same interests. Right now . . . he has a girlfriend, and that to me was a relief,

because that was just the clincher that he wasn't a girl."
The father said the boy was his son and that they spent
many evenings and weekends together hunting and fish-
ing. The boy's other recreational interest, shared with a
male friend, was motorbike racing in the dry river bed.
He said he experienced erotic arousal with his girlfriend.
When he learned that he could have a mastectomy and
remain a boy, he said, "I was very overjoyed."

Case Three: The child was raised a girl even though
her genitalia were masculinized. There was no surgical
intervention and her body began to masculinize—something she reacted to as a deformity. Cortisone therapy
was started at age twelve, releasing the ovaries to secrete
estrogen, and feminine body development followed,
though she was narrow in the hips from bone development influenced by the male hormone. At age twelve she
was operated on. She married fifteen years later, and
had a capacity for orgasm. She was fearful of rejection,
but the only physical reminders of her early masculinization were narrow hips, a small amount of coarse facial
hair, and a husky voice.

Cases Four and Five: The children were raised ambiguously due to parental confusion and poor medical
advice. There was no medical intervention before puberty, and both were hit with the full force of premature
masculinizing puberty. At the age of eight, the first child
was correctly diagnosed and sex reassignment surgery
was offered, but the child refused all communication.
After extraordinary attempts at explanation, the "boy"
finally left a note for the doctor, saying, "Dear Doctor, I
do not want to be a boy, I want to be a girl just [like] my
sisters." After cortisone therapy at age twelve, breast
growth began, the child was surgically feminized, and
she began to wear feminine clothing in public. She began to model herself explicitly on an older sister. She
married a year after her older sister and sought to become pregnant but miscarried due to failure to take
cortisone regularly.

The fifth child was raised as a girl from the age of two and a half years, but the local physician wrongly advised discontinuance of cortisone therapy, and the child became precociously masculine with a phallus of full adult size. By the age of eleven she looked like a mature boy of fourteen or fifteen, but wore dresses and a girl's hairstyle to school. When she was offered sex reassignment she opted to be a male, was operated on, and began hormone therapy. He began dating at fifteen and was exclusively romantically attracted to girls. He was able to talk about his new status in public, and his "appearance, demeanor, and behavior" were exclusively masculine.

Boy Raised As a Girl

Another of Money's cases[2] was a boy, one of normal identical twin boys, biologically male in every respect, who suffered a surgical mishap during circumcision by electrocautery at the age of seven months. His penis was cut off flush with the abdominal wall. After months of agonizing, the parents decided, when the boy was seventeen months old, to raise him as a girl, and doctors performed the first stages of feminizing surgery. The child was called Joan, wore girl's clothing and hairstyle, and the parents were regularly counselled how to raise her under the circumstances. Her mother made a special effort to keep her in dresses because she was initially resistant to them and preferred jeans. By the age of four she had a clear preference for dresses over slacks, wore bracelets and hair-ribbons, and took pride in her long hair. "She's very proud of herself when she puts on a new dress or I set her hair. She just loves to have her hair set; she could sit under the drier all day long," said her mother. Unlike her twin brother, she did not like to be dirty and seemed "daintier." "She likes me to wipe her face, yet I can't wash (her brother's) for anything." She was much tidier than her brother. At Christmas Joan asked for dolls, a doll's house, and a doll carriage. The boy wanted a garage with cars, gas pumps, and tools—

like his father. By the time they were five, the male twin wanted to be a "fireman or a policeman" . . . he wanted to do what daddy did . . . and to drive a car. But Joan wanted to be a doctor or a teacher and get married someday. She was tomboyish, had a lot of energy, and was often the dominant one in a girls' group; mother tried to teach her to be more ladylike. She had been the more dominant twin from the beginning, but her dominance over her brother was like that of a "mother hen," her mother said. The boy in turn "took up for his sister if anyone threatened her." The father reinforced different behavior in each of his children. Estrogen therapy was planned at puberty, and further surgery after that.

When the girl was about thirteen, she was interviewed by the British Broadcasting Corporation (BBC) and three psychiatrists, who concluded her gender identity was insecure. She refused to talk about sex. When asked to draw a human figure she drew a man because "women are too difficult." She complained that men had it good in life and women didn't. She had found it difficult to be accepted in her group of girls because she was not very attractive, and because her rather clumsy gait had gained her the nickname "cavewoman." She thought she would rather like to be a mechanic. The BBC panel thought that the transformation had been rather shaky, perhaps even inadvisable. It seemed the attempt to environmentally over-ride the basic biology was a failure and "Joan" became the subject of a scholarly fight between Money and other researchers who believed he should never have been brought up as a girl.[4] It all came to a head in early 1997[5] when it was revealed that at the time of the BBC interview the cat was already out of the bag—Joan had found out three years before that she was really a boy. A year before the program she had rejected hormone treatment for feminization. (No wonder she looked somewhat masculine.) A year after the program she began a two year program of penis reconstruction and began to call herself John. Eventually he married a woman several years his senior and adopted her children.

A confusing picture—but one that shows, nevertheless, that gender is not written into our genes or gonads. It is malleable and responds strongly to environmental signals. Before the "cat was out of the bag," the boy was behaving like the girl he was being raised to be. Afterwards he decided to co-operate with his genetic biology rather than suppress it medically, and he also began the corresponding psychological gender shift.

Ninety Percent Choose Gender of Upbringing

In a summary of all cases of intersexes that had come to their attention (particularly the work of the Hampsons), Money and Ehrhardt said about 90 percent chose to remain in their gender of upbringing in spite of contrary biology; that is, despite some or any of the following: contrary chromosomes, gonads, hormonal sex, internal sexual organs or external genital appearance.[3] They remark that of that 10 percent who changed their gender, almost all of them made a female to male change. Although the 90 percent established a gender identity consistent with their sex of choice, they did not do it without difficulty, embarrassment, and shame.

Biologically-Induced Gender Change?

Later researchers have taken issue with Money and Ehrhardt and the Hampsons, saying that humans are not blank slates at birth, but that there is a gender predisposition. One researcher, Milton Diamond, argues for a "prenatal (biological) organization," a "built-in bias with which a person interacts with his environment," but an extraordinary flexibility to adjust to an erroneously imposed gender.[6] Diamond also produced cases of gender identity chosen opposite to sex of rearing. So, too, did a group of researchers reporting on the deficiency of an enzyme called 5-α-reductase. This deficiency prevents formation of one of the male hormones, dihydrotestosterone,

so that the usual prenatal surge of testosterone that dif-
ferentiates a boy from a girl before birth does not occur,
and external genitalia are ambiguous. If the condition is
not diagnosed and treated, everyone gets a shock at
puberty when the testes become detectable and the body
becomes masculine. The researchers studied thirty-eight
of these cases in the Dominican Republic, particularly
eighteen who were "unambiguously raised as girls."[7] Their
findings? At puberty or after, seventeen of these children changed to a male gender identity and developed
an erotic interest in women. Many became heads of families. The researchers argued that androgens made a
"strong and definite contribution to male gender identity."

But the conclusion is not as straightforward as it
seems. Critics of the research argue that men had much
greater status and prestige in Dominican society, and
that together with sudden masculinization, a choice to be
male could be strongly culturally influenced. Certainly
the Dominican study seems to stand alone in the strength
of its argument for a hormonal basis to gender identity.
Another researcher into 5-α-reductase deficiency drew
an opposite conclusion. Gilbert Herdt, the most promi-
nent researcher among the Sambia of the eastern highlands of Papua New Guinea, found five cases of 5-α-
reductase deficiency in his study group.[8] In this case the
individuals were raised as girls but on their sudden
masculine development at marriageable age (puberty),
were treated as a third sex. Although the Sambia are a
strongly misogynist culture, there was no attempt—as in
the Dominican Republic—to adopt a male gender, because the culture forbade it; the Sambia believed a boy
could only become a man through ingestion of male
semen in prescribed regular fellatio in childhood. Herdt
argues that gender identity is therefore culture dependent rather than hormone dependent. Herdt also maintained that only thirteen in the Dominican Republic study,
not 17, lived unequivocally as men. In an almost identi-

cal condition found in the Gaza strip, only 28 percent changed gender at puberty.[9]

In the West, of those who have the 5-α-reductase deficiency, only a small percentage elect to change gender at puberty, and they find it difficult.[10] Ninety percent are content to remain in the gender of upbringing (female), possibly because the perceived rewards of being a Western woman are greater than in other cultures.

Summary

About 90 percent of intersexes on record elected to continue in the gender in which they were raised, even in the face of strongly contradictory biological and physical characteristics. If the influence of upbringing is so strong that it can over-ride obvious contrary biological predispositions, then it is clearly more powerful than biology in the development of gender identity. It becomes impossible to argue that gender identity in chromosomally normal individuals (like homosexuals) is in any way genetically or biologically enforced. In modern Western society, sexuality appears to be about 10 percent genetic and 90 percent environmental.

Notes

1. Vogt, H.J., "Sexual behavior in Klinefelter's syndrome." In *Klinefelter's Syndrome* edited by H.J. Bandmann, R. Breit, E. Perwein (Berlin: Springer-Verlag, 1984), 163-169.

2. Money, J., Ehrhardt, A.A., *Man & Woman, Boy & Girl* (Baltimore, MD: The Johns Hopkins University Press, 1972).

3. Hampson, J.L., Hampson, J.G., The ontogenesis of sexual behavior in man. In *Sex and Internal Secretions* edited by W.C. Young and G.W. Corner (Baltimore, MD: Williams and Wilkins, 1961), 1401-1432.

4. Diamond, M., "Sexual identity, monozygotic twins reared in discordant sex roles and a BBC follow-up," *Archives of Sexual Behavior* (1982), 11:181-186.

5. Diamond, M., Sigmundson, K.H., "Sex reassignment at birth: long term review and clinical implications," *Archives of Pediatric and Adolescent Medicine* (1997), 151:298-310.

6. Diamond, M., "A critical review of the ontogeny of human sexual behavior," *Quarterly Review of Biology* (1965), 40:147-175.

7. Imperato-McGinley, J., Peterson, R.E., Gautier, T., Sturla, E., "Androgens and the evolution of male-gender identity among males pseudohermaphrodites with 5 alpha-reductase deficiency," *The New England Journal of Medicine* (1979), 300:1233-1237.

8. Herdt, G., "Mistaken gender: 5-alpha reductase hermaphroditism and biological reductionism in sexual identity reconsidered," *American Anthropologist* (1990), 92:433-446.

9. Rösler, A., Kohn, G, "Male pseudohermaphroditism due to 17β-hydroxysteroid dehydrogenase deficiency: studies on the natural history of the defect and effect of androgens on gender role," *Journal of Steroid Biochemistry* (1983), 19:663-674.

10. Byne, W., Parsons, B., "Human sexual orientation. The biologic theories reappraised," *Archives of General Psychiatry* (1993), 50:228-239.

Chapter Six

What Do Different Cultures Tell Us about Sexual Preferences?

In 1994, an Italian-American geneticist, Cavalli-Sforza, published a huge genetic atlas,[1] the outcome of a monumental study of the genetic characteristics of different ethnic groups. He found that the human race was remarkably homogeneous, genetically. The more genes his team studied, the more they found all ethnic groups shared them. Cavalli-Sforza eventually studied fifty genes, all with effects on cell biochemistry, and found that all ethnic groups had most of those fifty genes. His conclusion was that, in spite of superficial differences (e.g. skin color), the different races are essentially the same genetically. In fact, something between 99.7 percent and 99.9 percent of the genes in any two unrelated people are the same.[2]

If all ethnic groups share almost all their genes, we can make two assumptions about any behavior that is claimed to be genetically determined:

• It will be very predictable, specific in nature and similar all over the globe.

• It will be present at roughly the same incidence in all cultures.

Now, let's recapitulate.

• Many genes, maybe hundreds, are involved in human behaviors.

• Behaviors affected by many genes will change very slowly over very many generations. That is, they will be very stable for centuries, with only minimal changes from generation to generation. This is true not only in families, but also in cultures.

If we look at homosexuality, we find none of the characteristics of genetic properties.

• There is a huge variety of homosexual practices between cultures and even within them.

• The incidence of homosexuality has varied considerably in different cultures. In some cultures, it has been unknown; in others, it has been obligatory for all males.

• There have been, and are, rapid changes in homosexual behavior—even over a lifetime. Not only that, but entire types of homosexuality have disappeared over the course of just a few centuries.

In fact, anthropologists have found such huge variations in heterosexual and homosexual practice from culture to culture, and such sudden changes in sexual practice and orientation, even over a single generation, that they mostly want to say that all sexual behavior is learned. In the words of one writer J. Rostand, "In the secret coming together of two human bodies, all society is the third presence."

Let's take a brief look at heterosexuality.

Variations In Heterosexual Customs

In 1952, two researchers, Ford and Beach,[3] reported the results of a project organized by Yale University, that surveyed 190 different cultures in a very large cross-cultural study. There was a wide range of heterosexual activity. There was no breast stimulation in six cultures; no kissing in nine; in two others, sexual excitement was correlated with scratching or biting; in one, urination was part of foreplay; in another, guest sex was practised (i.e., it was good hospitality to offer your wife to a visitor). Among the Lepchas, all young girls were sexually experienced by eleven or twelve, and even as young as eight. Bestiality occurred only erratically in cultures; in some it was unknown; in others, it was tolerated.

In a survey of preliterate cultures in 1971, Paul Gebhard[4] of the Kinsey Institute noted that fetishism, voyeurism, exhibitionism, and well-developed sadomasochism were very rare or absent, appearing only in more "advanced" societies.

What is sexually appealing in females depends on the culture. In Arabic culture, a fat woman is beautiful. In ours, a slim but well-rounded figure may be considered desirable. A broad pelvis is attractive in some cultures, a narrow one in others. In some cultures, the shape of the mouth is particularly sexy. In our culture, firm breasts are erotic; in others, pendulous breasts; in others the breasts are not erotic at all. In Japanese culture, there is a much greater erotic attraction to the nape of the neck and to older partners than in ours.

Even a superficial look at heterosexuality reveals a range of practices too broad to be genetically determined or strongly influenced.

Variations In Homosexuality

We have established that a genetically induced homosexuality would tend to be fairly uniform in expression throughout the world. But two entirely different types of behavior co-existed historically—the Greek model and the Melanesian model—and three co-exist today— the Greek model (secretly practised), the Melanesian model, and the Western model.[5] The variety of practices outside these models, and even within the Western model, are also quite at odds with a genetically prescribed homosexuality.

The Greek Model

At the height of the Greek culture, according to the social custom, an older married man was expected to take a younger boy as a kind of squire and have sexual relations with him. Today, the West would call him a

bisexual pederast. The older man would act as a mentor
to the young boy and train him in manhood. He would
even find the young boy a bride when he reached marriageable age. Then he would find another boy and start
the process again. As described by one scholar:[6] "This
sort of Greek male's ideal picture of himself was that he
serviced his wife, had a sexual friendship with his mis-
tress, and did his national duty by teaching younger men
how to behave with bravery and honor—which more or
less frequently involved buggering them in an idealistic
manner. It was only the boy he 'loved'." In the Greek
model, a boy starts out exclusively homosexual in his
relationship to his bisexual mentor, and then is strongly
encouraged to become bisexual at maturity.

In Greek culture, homosexuality between adults—as
we have it in the West today—was considered despicable
(mainly if one was the receptive partner). One classical
writer,[5] talking of the mature male who was also receptive, said, "we class those who enjoy the passive part as
belonging to the lowest depth of vice and allow them not
the least degree of confidence or respect or friendship."
Boys were not denigrated for being receptive—it was
appropriate to their status.

The Greek model[7] was found in early imperial Greece,
medieval Persia, and at various times in China and
Byzantium. It was found in the Sudan, in feudal Japan
among the samurai, and in the Libyan desert, where,
fifty years ago males "talked about their masculine love
affairs as openly as they discussed their love of women."[3]
The Mameluke rulers of Egypt imported young boys
from the Asian steppes. The Aztecs and Mayans also
subscribed to the Greek model. According to one account from the early 1900s, Arabic speakers in North
Morocco believed young boys would not learn the Koran
properly unless they had sexual relations with their teach-
ers. Sexual activity with boys or slaves was sometimes
regarded as a right among those with power and status.
Amongst the Big Nambas in Vanuatu, a father actively

sought 'guardians' for his sons who would mentor them and have sexual relationships with them.

The Melanesian Model

The Melanesian model[8] is not well known in the West. In it, men pass through three compulsory and sequential stages: passive exclusive homosexuality, active exclusive homosexuality, and exclusive adult heterosexuality. Many of the cultures practising it were in Papua New Guinea, and perhaps the best known group was called the Sambia (a pseudonym).

The Sambia believed that boys were naturally girl-like and would not develop manly qualities and sexual maturity unless they ingested semen. The culture required adolescents to fellate regularly (often daily) young boys after they were taken from their mothers at about age seven. When the boys reached the initiation rite at puberty, they then had to repeat the process with younger boys as their social duty. They continued to do this throughout adolescence, until they reached marriage-able age. Then they had to stop all homosexual activity, become exclusively heterosexual, and marry. Any man who still wished to engage in homosexual activity with those of his own age or younger was considered aberrant, a "rubbish man." Two such radical shifts in behavior in one lifetime would not be possible if homosexuality were genetically-mandated. One missionary familiar with the New Guinean tribal cultures (Don Richardson) suggests the prescribed homosexual behavior among youth might have been insisted upon by polygynous older men to keep youths away from the young girls they wanted as their own wives. Many anthropologists believe an extraordinary fear of contamination from women in this culture may have contributed to the practice (i.e., marriage was considered highly dangerous). Whatever the cause, anthropologists agree that it was culturally mandated.

The Melanesian model was found mostly in southern Papua New Guinea, and in the islands to the northeast. Overall, some 10-20 percent of Papua New Guinea cultures fell into this category. Sometimes the sexual expression was anal, sometimes oral. In some places, a youth was not permitted to fellate his friend, but could fellate his potential enemy. In others, boys were "grown" by friends within a group. In the Marind, an older youth who practised pederasty on a younger boy had to later marry that boy's sister, a practice also followed by the Etoro, Kiwai, and Keraki, except that in the latter two groups, sodomy was practised rather than fellatio.

The Western Model

The Western male homosexual model[5] is of comparatively recent origin and is quite different from either the Greek or Melanesian models, which institutionalized pederasty. The Western model is characterized by exclusive homosexuality between adults, usually of approximately equal status, and an insistence that the behavior is intrinsic. It is also highly politicized.

The first intimations of the Western model appear to have been adult homosexual networks in cities in France in the fifteenth and sixteenth centuries; for lesbians, some records date from the late 1700s. Homosexual relations between adults do occur in the historical record before that time, but the new element in the Western model is the relative absence of bisexuality and pederasty. Mollyhouses in England, in the 1700s, appear to be another pre-echo of modern homosexuality. These appear to have been essentially "adults only" houses of male prostitution, in which the receptive partners were very feminine in appearance.

Unlike other homosexual models, the Western model assumes homosexuality is not merely a behavior, but something innate to a person's real being. In the Western model, a person identifies himself as "homosexual," though the word was coined only late last century.

Greenberg[5] comments that modern western homosexuality implies that "erotic attraction originates in a relatively stable, more or less exclusive attribute of the individual," whereas in Western history or in non-Western forms of homosexuality, "distinctions of age . . . and social status loom larger." Modern lesbians, however, are uneasy about agreeing homosexuality is intrinsic, preferring in their commitment to the empowerment of women to see lesbianism as a choice.

The Western model tends to encourage promiscuity in males (AIDS has partially restrained this). A small subset of the male culture encourages a "monogamous" relationship with another adult, though usually with substantial amounts of "recreational sex" on the side. Bisexuality is often viewed as latent homosexuality; there is strong pressure to make a choice to be exclusively homosexual. The usual historical homosexual erotic attraction has been toward young boys, but there appears to be little of that among the modern gay community. However, there is significant interest in young post-pubertal teenagers, as far as is possible in Western countries, which universally proscribe it. Lesbianism has, until recently, placed considerably higher emphasis on sexual faithfulness among partners, though there is a recent new emphasis on sexual pleasure for its own sake. But even among the modern gay community, sexual expression varies from country to country; anal intercourse is more popular in some than others.

The modern homosexual movement is so unusual that some authors[7] have talked about "the uniqueness and particularity of the modern structuring of homosexuality into a gay world compared to precapitalist forms." For instance, in some cities, such as San Francisco, gays have created urban ghettoes—entire suburbs in which gays live and provide a full range of gay professional, social, and sexual services.

The Western model is, therefore, nearly unique historically. Its appearance has been too sudden, its evolution too swift, and spread too considerable to have been genetically produced. Its low incidence in some cultures, such as Arabic-speaking cultures, is also inconsistent with a genetically prescribed condition. The lesson of history and culture is that homosexuality is self-taught.

Not only are there quite different models—the Greek, Melanesian, and Western—co-existing today, but there are a myriad of other homosexual customs and practices—not the behavioral uniformity associated with a genetically dictated homosexuality.

More Permutations . . .

Among the polygynous Nyakusa (Lake Nyasa),[7] young men stopped herding cattle for fathers at a certain point, set up an all-bachelor village, and had homosexual relations. At age twenty-five, homosexuality was expected to stop and if a man could find a wife, he married. If any homosexuality continued, it was believed to be irrational and a sign of witchcraft.

Among the Nambutji of Central Australia, a man had a pederastic relationship with his future son-in-law for a while, then offered his daughter as a wife. Among the Nambikwara in Amazonia, brothers-in-law often had adolescent homosexual relations.

In modern, urban, Brazilian culture, an active homosexual partner tends to be viewed as a genuinely heterosexual man. But a passive male partner is viewed as another category of person altogether. In Brazilian Afro-American spiritist cults, males who are mediums take a passive role in homosexual intercourse. They are called "bichas." But if two bichas become sexually involved, they are known as "lesbians."[9]

Many North American Indian tribes recognized people called "berdaches." Male berdaches were classed as "not-men," a kind of third sex.[10] They were distinct from women, although they had many feminine characteristics and occupations and wore feminine-type attire. They were often believed to have shamanistic or healing powers. Sex with other "not-men" was completely forbidden, though sex with other men was permitted. In some cultures, berdaches could only have sex with women.

In the Congo, among the Basongye in the Masai oriental province, there are berdache-like people called "bitesha." The males are transvestite (wear feminine clothing), but heterosexual. They tend to be musically inclined and take female work roles. Similarly, females who reject the role of women (but still wear women's clothes), are also "bitesha" and marry male "bitesha." There is no lesbianism.

Among the Chuckchee (North Siberia), homosexuality was compulsory but did not rule out heterosexual relations.[10] Among the Iban (West Africa), married heterosexual men were expected later to be involved homosexually.

Lesbianism

Although genetic determination or influence in homosexuality would mean it would occur in all cultures, Ford and Beach[3] recorded only seventeen cultures in which lesbianism was known at all, and the behaviors were all quite different.

The Nyakusa (Lake Nyasa) polygynous society had a system in which the wives lived in huts relatively near each other, and there was some lesbianism among cowives—permitted rather than prescribed. The husbands of these women generally did not like the lesbianism but seldom did much to repress it. In general, lesbianism is fairly well known within harems wherever they exist.

Adolescent Dahomey girls, as a preparation for heterosexual marriage, toughened their genitalia in sexual activities together.

There was an instance of partially institutionalized lesbianism between about 1865 and 1935 in the Pearl River Delta in Southern Kwangtung, (Canton) in China.[11] Essentially, it was a marriage-resistance movement. The silk industry gave financial independence to about

100,000 women who lived together in Buddhist vegetarian halls, sometimes as sworn sisters, and sometimes in explicitly sexual relationships. It was tolerated by the outside society, but relationships within the community were often unstable and somewhat violent.

In Lesotho, while the men were absent, usually working in South Africa, adolescent girls and young women engaged in a sexual intimacy called "Mummies and Babies,"[12] because one partner tended to mother the other. Like the Dahomey example, it preceded heterosexual marriage and had marriage in mind. The movement started in the 1950s and continued for decades. It was compatible with heterosexuality.

Cultures without Homosexuality

If homosexuality were significantly influenced, let alone dictated, by genes, it would appear in every culture, but in twenty-nine of seventy-nine cultures surveyed by Ford and Beach in 1952,[3] homosexuality was rare or absent. It was very rare in the Siriono, even though there were no prohibitions on homosexual relationships in that culture. The researcher observed only one man displaying slight homosexual traits but apparently not sexually involved with another man. Homosexuality appears to be rare among Orthodox Jews,[13] so much so that learned rabbis, the interpreters of Jewish law, usually allowed men to sleep in the same bed, because likelihood of sexual contact was considered negligible. Kinsey also found very low homosexual incidence among Orthodox Jews.[14]

Some anthropologists have questioned Ford and Beach's findings, believing that irregular sexual intimacy is not something foreign researchers can easily get information about. One anthropologist, Whitam,[15] thought homosexuality must be genetically enforced because he found it practised in some isolated groups in South America and East Asia who knew nothing of the practice elsewhere.

But evidence from other remote tribes in New Guinea—all genetically related—suggests differently. For example, in contrast to groups like the Sambia in the New Guinea highlands, where homosexuality was compulsory, only about 2-3 percent of Western Dani (also in the New Guinea highlands) practiced it. However, in another group of Dani who were genetically related, homosexuality was totally unknown. Missionaries report that when they were translating the Bible into Dani for this group, their tribal assistants, who knew their own culture intimately, were nonplused by references to homosexuality in Romans 1; they did not understand the concept. Another missionary, with the same group for 25 years, overheard many jests and sexually ribald exchanges among the men, but never a single mention of homosexuality in all that time. When Dani went to help with missionary work among the Sambia, they were astounded at some of the homosexual practices they saw for the first time. Although it is always difficult for a foreigner to be completely sure whether a rare and stigmatized behavior exists, it is certainly true that if three such different experiences of homosexuality can occur in groups of people so closely related genetically, genetic determinism of homosexuality is an impossibility.

Sudden Changes

We have mentioned that human behaviors associated with many genes change slowly over many generations or centuries. But history shows us that homosexual practice has disappeared quite suddenly—in some cases over a couple of generations—as the culture has changed.

For example, there were many berdaches among the North American Crows in 1840, but by 1900 only one was left. Among the Potowatami, there was a huge decrease in berdaches between 1870 and 1930. The transvestite Koniags of Kodiak Island disappeared between 1800 and 1850. The "men turned women" (*manang bali*) of Borneo were common in 1850, rare in 1911, and are now unknown. The Samurai and their practices vanished long ago. Among the Aymara (South American), the homosexuality, lesbianism, and transvestism recorded in historical times has now disappeared. Tahitian mahus are far less common now than in the late eighteenth century. Anthropologists attribute many of the changes to Christian influence. In some cases, homosexuality disappeared so rapidly that accurate information on homosexual practices was hard to collect. The customs of the Sambia vanished, under missionary teaching, about 1984. Even at the height of the Sambian pederastic culture, the sudden change required of men of marriageable age from homosexuality to heterosexuality argued against its being genetically innate, and in favor of a substantial cultural basis to homosexual orientation and practice.

But change was not always missionary-mediated. Men's houses, besides being homosexual hot-houses, were also venues for planning war raids. In some cases, the government stepped in and simply closed the houses down, sometimes jailing offenders. This worked; it also completely disrupted and contributed to the disappearance of pederastic activity in a few years.

The Greek model (cultural pederasty), after having become popular in Rome, disappeared slowly with time as the culture absorbed several ascetic philosophies. There was a further decline after the Christianization of the Roman Empire. But even this change over a few centuries was probably too sudden for a genetically dominated behavior. The sudden rise and disappearance of lesbian practices, such as the Pearl River communities and the "Mummies and Babies" movements, were incompatible with any genetic model.

Even within the modern gay scene, there have been changes in practice, which have been far too swift for anything genetically induced. Fisting (insertion of the hand into the rectum) was virtually unknown in the forties and fifties, but a large minority of gays (at least in San Francisco[16]) have now experienced it at least once, and the practice has spread to lesbians with both anal and vaginal expression. Feminine mannerisms have decreased among male homosexuals, and a recent trend has been an exaggerated maleness.

Summary

When Greenberg comments that "it is reasonable to suppose that if a bunch of Melanesian infants were to be transported in infancy to the United States and adopted, few would seek out the pederastic relationships into which they're inducted in New Guinea," he summarizes the essence of this chapter. If sexual behavior were genetically determined, or even strongly prompted, the Melanesian infants would seek out pederastic relationships in their new culture.

The diversity in homosexual activity in different cultures also argues against genetic enforcement. If homosexuality were genetically mandated, the type of homosexual behavior would be tightly defined by the genes involved and almost uniform in all cultures. If we want to argue genetic homosexuality, Vines' report that the human race shares more than 99.7 percent of its genes[2] means that between 60 and 200 genes would have to account for all the variation in homosexual practice that exists globally, in addition to all other differences. This is highly unlikely.

If homosexuality were genetic in origin, it would appear at about the same incidence in all cultures. But this is clearly not so. Among the genetically related tribes of the New Guinea Highlands, homosexuality was simultaneously practiced as mandatory pederasty among the Sambia, was unknown in another group even as a concept, and practiced by 2-3 percent of a related group. A significant number of cultures appear not to have practised homosexuality at all.

The rate of change of homosexual practice also argues against genetic causation. Slight changes in practice would appear over 1000 years if there were some strong genetic pressure for it, but not the extensive decline of whole models over several centuries (e.g., the Greek model), not the entire disappearance of homosexuality from some cultures over several generations, and certainly not the relatively sudden rise of the modern Western model, with characteristics so different from its predecessors and its own swiftly changing practices.

The expression of homoerotic desire does not seem to be genetically informed or dictated. Sexuality appears to have an overwhelmingly cultural component, ebbing and flowing with changes in cultural values and expectations. Certain sexual expressions may be historical phenomena which flourish for a time because of particular circumstances, and then cease (e.g., Pearl River lesbianism). Pederastic homosexuality can be culturally mandated, as among the Sambia, or culturally proscribed, as in the West.

When anthropologists survey the evidence, they are, to a surprising degree, united in the belief that behaviors such as homosexuality and lesbianism are not produced genetically, but by social conditions. If they tried to put a figure on the genetic content of homosexuality, most of them would probably argue for something near zero.

Did their genes make them do it? Not according to the anthropologists.

Notes

1. Cavalli-Sforza, L.L., Menozzi, P., Piazza, A., *The History and Geography of Human Genes* (Princeton, NJ: Princeton University Press, 1994).

2. Vines, G., "Genes in black and white," *New Scientist*, (July 1995), 34-37.

3. Ford, C.S., Beach, F.A., *Patterns of Sexual Behavior* (London: Eyre and Spottiswoode, 1952).

4. Gebhard, P.H., *Human Behavior: Variations in the Ethnographic Spectrum* (New York: Basic Books, 1971).

5. Greenberg, D.F., *The Construction of Homosexuality* (Chicago: The University of Chicago Press, 1988).

6. Seymour-Smith, M., *Sex and Society* (London: Hodder and Stoughton, 1975).

7. Adams, B.D., "Age, structure, and sexuality-reflections on the anthropological evidence on homosexual relations." In *The Many Faces of Homosexuality: Anthropological Approaches to Homosexual Behavior* edited by E. Blackwood (New York: Harrington Park Press, 1986), 19-33.

8. Herdt, G.H., "Guardians of the Flutes," *Idioms of Masculinity* (New York: McGraw-Hill, 1981).

9. Fry, P., "Male homosexuality and spirit possession in Brazil." In *The Many Faces of Homosexuality: Anthropological Approaches to Homosexual Behavior* edited by E. Blackwood (New York: Harrington Park Press, 1986), 137-153.

10. Callender, C., "Men and Non-Men- Male gender-mixing statuses and homosexuality." In *The Many Faces of Homosexuality: Anthropological Approaches to Homosexual Behavior* edited by E. Blackwood (New York: Harrington Park Press, 1986), 165-178.

11. Sankar, A., "Sisters and brothers, lovers and enemies-marriage resistance in Southern Kwangtung." In *The Many Faces of Homosexuality: Anthropological Approaches to Homosexual Behavior* edited by E. Blackwood (New York: Harrington Park Press, 1986), 69-81.

12. Gay, J., "Mummies and Babies and friends and lovers in Lesotho." In *The Many Faces of Homosexuality: Anthropological Approaches to Homosexual Behavior* edited by

E. Blackwood (New York: Harrington Park Press, 1986), 97-116.

13. Prager, D., Judaism, Homosexuality and Civilization, *Ultimate Issues* (1990), 6:24.

14. Kinsey, A.C., Pomeroy, W.B., Martin, C.E., *Sexual Behavior in the Human Male* (Philadelphia: W.B. Saunders, 1948).

15. Whitam, F.L., Mathy, R.M., *Male Homosexuality in Four Societies. Brazil, Guatemala, the Philippines, and the United States* (New York: Praeger, 1986).

16. Cameron, P., *Medical Consequences of What Homosexuals Do* (Washington, DC: Family Research Council, 1992).

Chapter Seven

Does Pre-natal Hormonal Exposure Make You Homosexual?

Many people have wondered if homosexuality is fixed or influenced by exposure in the womb to unusual levels of male or female hormones. The theory is that if a male embryo is exposed to lower than normal levels of male hormones, or a female embryo to excess male hormones, the child may grow up homosexual. Such exposure to sex hormones may make lower animals bisexual.

In normal development, it takes a natural surge of testosterone in the embryo to turn the female reproductive tracts into male sex organs. You could say that the default sexuality in the womb is female, and that, without the testosterone surge (and the action of another hormonal substance that inhibits the normal development of female organs), the embryo would remain female. Normally, a trace of a female sex hormone, estradiol, is also needed for growth in the uterus of both male and female babies.

Treatments for medical conditions during pregnancy and certain rare hormonal conditions in humans have given researchers opportunity to study the effect of high or low levels of male and female hormones on the embryo in the womb and on later sexual orientation. We will look at four of them.

Exposure to Diethylstilbestrol

Between about 1940 and 1970, diethylstilbestrol, an artificial female sex hormone, was given to pregnant mothers at risk of miscarriage. (It is no longer administered because of increased risks of genital cancer in daughters and sons of these women). Research on female guinea pigs had shown a link between synthetic female hormone and sexual behavior, though not in an expected direction. It led to increased masculine sexual behavior in female guinea pigs. It also led—more predictably—to decreased masculine behavior in male rats. Researchers wondered if the same effects might be found in humans.

The doses of diethylstilbestrol given to women in the study were very high: 5-250 mg. per day. In much later research, the children of these women were queried in detail about their sexual orientation in the previous eighteen months: fantasies, romantic/sexual daydreams, and many other detailed tests.[1] In two studies, there was slightly more lesbianism than in the controls (a normal comparison group), but two earlier studies found no difference in sexual orientation. A fifth study, the latest and most definitive,[2] showed no difference. So, the girls were exposed to levels of female hormone far in excess of anything a fetus would naturally be exposed to, and, even at those very high levels, no effect was found.

A study of twenty boys,[3] exposed to diethylstilbestrol in the womb, showed that none had homosexual tendencies (though one of the non-exposed controls did). This suggests that pre-natal exposure to this hormone does not lead to homosexuality in men.

Adrenogenital Syndrome

When girls are exposed to male hormones in the womb, one outcome is adrenogenital syndrome. You met adrenogenital syndrome in chapter five. To recapitulate briefly: in the development of a female fetus, the adrenal glands normally produce a hormone called cortisol which is involved in control of protein and carbohydrate metabolism. In adrenogenital syndrome, because of an enzyme deficiency, an androgen is produced instead. Girls exposed in the uterus to this hormone develop unusually large clitorises (more like miniature phalluses), and, if the condition is untreated, can grow up looking very masculine. These days, females with this condition are given life-long drug treatment to counteract the masculinizing effect of the continuing androgen production. However, forty years ago, girls with this condition were sometimes left untreated, and researchers have studied them to find effects on sexual orientation.

Earlier studies showed no effect on sexual orientation, but one study by Money, Schwartz, and Lewis[4] came up with a large group (37 percent) who were bisexual, but not lesbian, which seemed to show a large influence on sexual orientation. However, a survey of diabetic patients matched with the girls for age and hospital experience came up with identical levels of bisexuality. Unless we argue that diabetes also causes bisexuality, it would appear that common environmental factors in the two groups might have been responsible. These girls were frequently hospitalized[5] and subjected to much medical scrutiny and interviewed about their sexuality. The Money, Schwartz, and Lewis study has also been criticized for poor interviewing techniques, which over-estimated the bisexuality of the respondents.[6] For example, girls with this syndrome who are untreated are acutely embarrassed about themselves and often unwilling to talk about sex at all. In this study, they did not feel feminine and did not have boyfriends. Some of this may have been interpreted as bisexuality, by default. In chapter three, we mentioned gender nonconformity as one of the strongest predictors of future homosexuality. These girls felt very different from their peers. They were particularly conscious of their excessive hairiness, which they said was the one thing they would like changed more than anything—even their deep voices.

Environmental factors appear to override hormonal influences, according to another study;[7] no correlation was found between masculine behavior in girls with adrenogenital syndrome and increased physical masculinization. In still another study, lesbianism seemed to be associated with poor vaginal function, in which the girls doubted their femininity.[8]

Boys can also have this condition. They are simply exposed to more male hormones than usual. This might be expected to completely eliminate homosexuality. But, in the sample of thirty, one experienced homosexual attraction.[9] This level (3%) is not significantly different from the incidence of homosexuality in the normal population. The sample is too small to say much more, except that exposure in the uterus to excess masculinizing hormone clearly does not eliminate homosexual orientation in males.

These results disproved the theory of pre-natal exposure to excess hormones as a cause of homosexuality. Exposure to excess androgen had no effect on boys, and a doubtful effect on girls. The girls were exposed in the womb to one of the strongest doses of male hormones known in the scientific record, but apparently became doubtfully bisexual rather than lesbian. What, then, can possibly be producing lesbianism in females experiencing normal conditions in the womb? Not exposure to pre-natal hormones, it seems.

In a lesser known, 1974, study of eighteen young women in Soviet Russia who had adrenogenital syndrome, none showed the slightest trace of lesbianism or lesbian erotic fantasy.[10] The author attributed this to stricter mores in the Soviet Union. Regardless, it seems the result is sensitive to social setting.

Androgen Insensitivity Syndrome

What would happen if a chromosomal male (XY) was not exposed to any androgen at all in the womb? If anything hormonal was going to produce homosexuality in a male child, you would think this would be it. But instead the child develops as a girl, with a heterosexual orientation. The fetus remains feminine because the testosterone surge does not occur. Androgen insensitivity syndrome is a rare condition in which the cells in the developing male fetus lack the receptors for the hormone testosterone, meaning that, however much is produced by the testes, the cells will not respond to it. Children are, therefore, born with external female genitalia, but have testes in the abdominal cavity. However, the cells do seem to be sensitive to female sex hormones, because breasts and typical female shape develop at puberty (under the influence of traces of female sex hormones produced by the testes!), but, because there are no ovaries, there are no menses, and the condition is usually discovered only at that point. These people otherwise are brought up as females. They develop a female gender identity and a sexual attraction toward men. Their patterns of sexual arousal and kinds of erotic imagery are indistinguishable from normal females.[4]

A rare condition with similar effects is called 17α-hydroxylase deficiency. The absence of a particular enzyme in the production pathway for male hormones means that neither the adrenal glands nor the testes produce any male hormone at all. Such a person looks like a girl when born. Without intervention, he also grows up indistinguishable from a girl.[11]

Maternal Stress

In rats, researchers have found a link between maternal stress and demasculinizing effects in the sexual behavior of male offspring. The mother's stress leads to a delayed testosterone surge in male rats. An East German researcher, Dörner, claimed to have found a similar effect in humans during the Second World War. If mothers underwent strong stress, he found no heterosexuality in their young offspring, 25 percent bisexuality, and 35 percent homosexuality. The remainder were too young to know what their preferences were.[12]

These were spectacular results, but the study appears to be maverick. Other studies on rats could not find the effect, and stress in human mothers delays the testosterone surge much less markedly than in rats. Dörner has also been criticized for not interviewing the mothers.[12] Three other studies on humans did not find any effect. The latest and most sophisticated of the three studies, although it found no correlations with stress for boys, did find a relatively strong correlation between homosexual fantasy and childhood gender non-conformity[12] (see chapter three). Curiously, in this study, there was a moderate correlation for girls between maternal stress and lesbianism, which made no sense to the authors. Girls are not exposed to a pre-natal testosterone surge, so a delayed surge makes no sense in this context.

A still more recent study[13] repeated Dörner's study with people in the most stressed of all German cities, but found no increased rates of homosexuality.

Adult Exposure to Sex Hormones

Do sex hormone drugs given to adults have any effect on sexual orientation?

It was long believed that homosexuals had lower levels of testosterone (male hormone), or higher levels of estrogen (female hormone) in their bodies, and that lesbians had higher levels of testosterone and lower estrogen levels. The corrective step appeared to be administration of counter-balancing doses of whatever hormone was necessary. But it didn't work. Male homosexuals given male hormones only became more sexually active, not more heterosexual. So doctors experimented with doses of estrogen in the thirties to see if they stimulated androgen feedback responses. The father of computer science, Alan Turing, arrested for homosexual activities, was required to take estrogen. It had no apparent effect.[14] Courts ordering men to undergo hormonal treatment to change their orientation eventually stopped the practice as it became clear it was ineffective.

In the literature, as reviewed by Meyer-Bahlburg, three studies suggested testosterone levels were lower in male homosexuals, twenty found levels in homosexuals were the same as in heterosexuals, and two found elevated levels in homosexuals.[15] Another reviewer of the biomedical literature, Louis Gooren, remarks, "Not only have the best designed studies failed to find differences in hormone levels between homosexuals and heterosexuals, but . . . the scientific principles of endocrinology do not make that plausible."[3] Nor, he commented has it ever "been reported that sexual orientation underwent a shift induced by the change of levels of androgens and estrogens."

On the other hand, there is plenty of evidence that hormonal therapy raises or inhibits existing sex drive. Rates of sexual fantasy and orgasm more than tripled in one group of men being treated with androgen for very low levels of testosterone.[16] This is one of the strongest effects on record for heightened libido. A similar test of women on estrogen replacement therapy showed about a 20 percent increase in libido compared with controls.[17] Androgens also increase libido in women when they are given to combat advanced breast cancer.[18]

Some drugs decrease libido. Oral contraceptives tend to lower sex drive by about 30 percent, according to one study.[19] But, even in those cases, habits and mental attitudes can overrule. Even with chemical castration recommended for some sex offenders, some criminal behavior persisted because of mental habits that had been established. In one classic study, in which men were treated with estrogens and anti-androgens,[20] some criminal sexual behavior continued even though sexual activity dropped to about 25 percent of normal, and interest to about 60 percent. Even physical castration has equivocal effects for many offenders. For some, sexual fantasy and performance decrease quite rapidly—in one study of 2500 sex offenders, repeated offences fell from 50 percent to 3.5 percent—but a small minority continued to be as sexually active as ever.[21] It is still possible for castrated men, paraplegics, or eunuchs to have mental orgasms.[22] But generally apathy sets in.

As one reviewer of the literature on hormones and libido comments, "The available literature suggests that humans have not escaped completely from the endocrinological control of sexual behavior and that humans are similar in certain ways to the other mammals. On the other hand it is also obvious that social learning plays an extremely important role in human sexual behavior."[18]

The Placebo Effect

Hormonal effects are often small compared with the effects of mental attitudes. People who think a treatment is going to work often show improvement even though the treatment is proven ineffective. This is called the placebo effect. Placebos are inactive substances, without physical curative effects, which are often used in drug trials. For this reason, double-blind trials are now the rule when drugs are being tested: neither the patient nor the researcher knows who received the placebo and who received the prescribed drug. Studies of the effect of drugs on libido are subject to a strong placebo effect—people who believe the treatment will raise libido often show increased sex drive, suggesting that state of mind is one of the most powerful influences on human sexuality.

One researcher of the effect of hormones on libido was notorious for insisting that a preparation of monkey testicles had revolutionized his sex life. Only later did researchers learn that the testicles had been prepared in such a way that any sex hormones had been thoroughly eradicated. The effect was all in the mind. "Very many suggested effects on libido are anecdotal, and doubtful, and may arise from increases in general well-being," says one researcher in the field.[23]

Summary

Although there are some pre-natal hormonal effects on sexual behavior for lower animals, there is not convincing evidence for such an effect on sexual orientation in humans. The studies examining the effects of high doses of female hormones to pregnant women are particularly informative because these are very high doses and any hormonal effects on sexual orientation should show up clearly. But the result is a dubious effect on women and no effects on men. Any effects on sexual orientation appear to be better explained in terms of gender non-conformity—a psychological construct. Sex drugs do increase or lower sex drive, but that appears to be about all.

We leave the last word to several researchers in the field. "In summary, the evidence from prenatal endocrine disorders and from the offspring of hormone-treated pregnancies suggests that hormones may contribute to, but do not actually determine, the course of sexual orientation in individuals with an abnormal sex-steroid history during prenatal life."[3] "At this time, the literature does not support a causal link between hormones and homosexuality."[10]

So, not only your genes didn't make you do it, it seems your hormones didn't either. In sexual orientation, the strongest stimulation appears to come from the mind and the environment.

Notes

1. Ehrhardt, A.A., Meyer-Bahlburg, H.F.L., Feldman, J.F., Ince, S.E. "Sex-dimorphic behavior in childhood subse-

quent to prenatal exposure to exogenous progestogens and estrogens," *Archives of Sexual Behavior* (1984), 13:457-479.

2. Lish, J.D., Meyer-Bahlburg, H.F.L., Ehrhardt, M., Travis, B.G., Veridiano, N.P., "Prenatal exposure to di-ethylstilbestrol (DES): childhood play behavior and adult gender-role behavior in women," *Archives of Sexual Behavior* (1992), 21:423-441.

3. Gooren, L., "Biomedical Theories of Sexual Orientation: A Critical Examination." In *Homosexuality/Heterosexuality* edited by D.P. McWhirter, A.S. Sanders, and J.M. Reinisch (New York: Oxford University Press, 1990), 71-87.

4. Money, J., Schwartz, M., Lewis, V.G., "Adult erotosexual status and fetal hormonal masculinization and demasculinization: 46, XX congenital virilizing adrenal hyperplasia and 46, XY androgen-insensitivity syndrome compared," *Psychoneuroendocrinology* (1984), 9:405-414.

5. Vines, G., "Obscure origins of desire," *New Scientist*, (28 November 1992): 2-8.

6. McConaghy, N., "Heterosexuality/Homosexuality: dichotomy or continuum," *Archives of Sexual Behavior* (1987), 16:411-424.

7. Dittmann, R.W., Kappes, M.H., Kappes, M.E., Borger, D., Stegner, H., Willig, R.H., Wallis, H., "Congenital adrenal hyperplasia. I. Gender-related behavior and attitude in female patients and sisters," *Psychoneuroendocrinology* (1990), 15:401-420.

8. Mulaikal, R.M., Migeon, C.J., Rock, J.A., "Fertility rates in female patients with congenital adrenal hyperplasia due to 21-hydroxylase deficiency," *The New England Journal of Medicine* (1987), 316:178-182.

9. Money, J, Lewis, V., "Homosexual/heterosexual status in boys at puberty: idiopathic adolescent gynecomastia

and congenital virilizing adrenocorticism compared," *Psychoneuroendocrinology* (1982), 7:339-346.

10. Banks, A., Gartrell, N.K., "Hormones and sexual orientation: a questionable link," *Journal of Homosexuality* (1995), 30:247-268.

11. Money, J., Ehrhardt, A.A., *Man & Woman, Boy & Girl* (Baltimore, MD: The Johns Hopkins University Press, 1972).

12. Bailey, J.M., Willerman, L., Parks, C., "A test of the maternal stress theory of human male homosexuality," *Archives of Sexual Behavior* (1991), 20:277-293.

13. Schmidt, G., Clement, U., "Does peace prevent homosexuality?" *Journal of Homosexuality* (1995), 30:269-275.

14. Murphy, T.F., "Redirecting sexual orientation: techniques and justifications," *The Journal of Sex Research* (1992), 29:501-523.

15. Meyer-Bahlburg, H.F.L., "Psychoendocrine research on sexual orientation: current status and future options," *Progress in Brain Research* (1984), 61:375-398.

16. Kwan, M., Greenleaf, W.J., Mann, J., Crapo, L., Davidson, J.M., "The nature of androgen action on male sexuality—a combined laboratory-self-report study on hypogonadal men," *Journal of Clinical Endocrinology and Metabolism* (1983), 57:557-562.

17. Dennerstein, L., Burrows, G.D., "Hormone replacement therapy and sexuality in women," *Clinics in Endocrinology and Metabolism* (1982), 11:661-679.

18. Segraves, R.T., "Hormones and libido." In: *Sexual Desire Disorders* edited by S.R. Lieblum and R.C. Rosen (New York: The Guilford Press, 1988), 271-312.

19. Leeton, J., McMaster, R., Worsley, A., "The effects on sexual response and mood after sterilization of women taking long-term oral contraception: results of a double-

blind cross-over study," *Australian and New Zealand Journal of Obstetrics and Gynecology* (1978), 18:194-197.

20. Bancroft, J., Tennent, G., Loucas, K., Cass, J., "The control of deviant sexual behavior by drugs: 1. Behavioral changes following Estrogens and Anti-Androgens," *British Journal of Psychiatry* (1974), 125:310-315.

21. Cameron, P., *The Gay Nineties* (Franklin, TN: Adroit Publishers, 1993).

22. Money, J., "Sex hormones and other variables in human eroticism," In *Sex and Internal Secretions* edited by W.C. Young and G.W. Corner (Baltimore, MD: Williams and Wilkins, 1961), 1383-1400.

23. Segraves, R.T., "Drugs and desire," In *Sexual Desire Disorders* edited by S.R. Lieblum and R.C. Rosen (New York: The Guilford Press, 1988), 313-347.

Are Brains "Gay"?

Is it possible that the brain of a homosexual person is different from the brain of a heterosexual person? Is sexuality somehow hard-wired into the micro-structure of the brain?

We explained in chapter eight that, as a child grows in the womb, it will be subjected to a sudden strong surge of testosterone if it is a boy, so that the male reproductive organs will develop. This sudden surge also results in a spurt of growth in the brain. It seems quite possible, therefore, that a boy's brain will be different from a girl's, and that the brain of a homosexual may be different from either, or maybe more like the brain of the opposite sex. Such a finding would suggest that sexual orientation is built in.

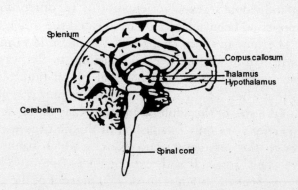

Figure 13: Brain Structure (viewed from right side)

In the seventies and eighties, researchers began to look for microscopic sex differences in the brain. Now, reports of structural sex differences abound, but the only consistently replicable finding is that the brain is larger in men than in women.[1] Some research has focused on clusters of cells in a part of the brain called the hypothalamus—more particularly, on a cluster of cells in the hypothalamus called the INAH-3. Three out of four studies have found it to be larger in men than in women.[1] But it was a study of the hypothalamus, in 1991, that generated most interest and controversy. A gay scientist, LeVay, formerly of the Salk Institute, claimed that the INAH-3 was smaller in homosexual men than in heterosexual men;[2] in other words, it was more like a woman's.

LeVay and the Hypothalamus

Problems with LeVay's Research

Brain Changes in Response to Learning and Activity

Although he originally commented about his findings: "It's one more nail in the coffin of critics who argue that homosexuality is a choice and thus immoral,"[3] when he is pressed, LeVay is more moderate. He says "the results do not allow one to decide if the size of the INAH-3 in an individual is the cause or consequence of that individual's sexual orientation."[2] In other words, homosexual behavior could have created the difference.

The human brain changes at the micro-level in response to the way we live: to learning, to the way we behave, and to all sorts of habitual stimulation. Shatz[4] says that when a baby is born, its brain is only one quarter of the size of the adult brain, and many of the neural connections are only established in the first three years through the stimulation and exercise which babies receive. This proceeds with extraordinary intensity; after only *one* year the brain is already 70 percent of the adult size.

It is fair to say the brain is like a computer which is trying to program itself. Neurons fire at random, and, if the result is reinforced, the path becomes fairly permanent, though not set in concrete. If it is not reinforced, the path becomes hard to excite. Extensive stimulation is needed or pathways do not develop, and some periods are more important for certain kinds of stimulation than others. For example, if a child is deprived of light to the eyes in a critical early period, it develops childhood cataracts and becomes blind. If an adult is deprived of light for a few weeks, no such damage happens.[4]

Changes also take place in the adult brain. Monkey experiments have shown that artificial exercise of three digits on the hand increases the area of the brain associated with those fingers and decreases the other regions proportionately.[5] Violinists have a grossly enlarged area of the brain devoted to the fingers of their left hands.

We change our brains at the micro-level through the way we exercise, and anything we do repetitively especially if associated with pleasure (e.g.) sexual activity. So, if LeVay did find real differences in the brains of his subjects, it is quite possible they were the result of homosexual activity. But there are other difficulties with LeVay's findings.

The Unknown Sexual Orientation of His Control Sample

The sexual orientation of LeVay's homosexual sample is not in doubt, but the sexual orientation of his "heterosexual" control sample was not known. Two had denied homosexual activity, but there was no information on the other fourteen. They were "presumed heterosexual." How do we know? Six of that "presumed heterosexual" control group were known to have died of AIDS. That is, 37.5 percent, compared with less than 0.0001 percent of the general heterosexual population.[6]

The problems show up in Figure 14. The measure on the right is the volume of the INAH-3 in cubic millimeters. If the discs in the vertical column marked *M* (those "presumed heterosexuals" who died of AIDS) are added to the homosexual group (column HM) the distinction between the groups is no longer statistically significant. In other words, the brains of homosexual men no longer cluster in the minimum range; the alleged distinction disappears.

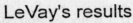

LeVay's results

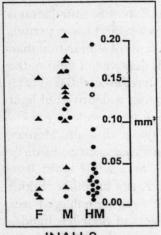

INAH-3

F = Females
M = Presumed heterosexual males
HM = Homosexual males

● Individuals who died of complications of AIDS
▲ Individuals who died of causes other than AIDS
○ Bisexual male who died of AIDS

Figure 14:

But even if LeVay's presumed heterosexual sample is all heterosexual, there is still a considerable overlap in the sizes of the INAH-3 in homosexual and heterosexual men. In fact, a heterosexual man had one of the smallest clusters in the sample, three homosexuals had larger clusters than the mean size for heterosexuals, and three heterosexual men had smaller clusters than the mean size for homosexual men. These "outliers" are exceptions that undermine any claims about the determinative nature of the size of the INAH-3.

Reprinted with permission from LeVay, S. "A Difference in Hypothalamic Structure Between Heterosexual Men." *Science*, (1991) 253: 1034-1037.

The INAH-3's Link with Sexual Behavior is Only Postulated

The region in the brain of the rat that LeVay believes is analogous to the INAH-3 in humans can be totally destroyed with no observable effects on sexual behavior.[7] The INAH-3 may turn out to have some connection with sexual behavior in humans, but, at the moment, that has not been proven.

The Results Have Not Been Replicated

A much more careful repetition of LeVay's study was done by Byne.[8] It included "blind" work; in other words, the researchers who looked at the cells of the INAH-3 under the microscope had no idea whether the subject was a man or woman, gay or straight. The study did confirm that there was a real male-female difference in the size of INAH-3 cells. But it did not find LeVay's difference between gay and straight brains.

The Suprachiasmatic Nucleus

There has also been a report that the size of another cluster of cells in the hypothalamus, the suprachiasmatic nucleus, is larger in homosexual men than in heterosexual men.[9] But the study has never been corroborated, and probably won't be, according to two experts in the field, Byne and Parsons,[10] who maintain that the size of this nucleus in humans does not vary with sex, and is therefore even less likely to vary with sexual orientation. "Few studies of this sort have proved to be replicable in the past," they say.

The Brain Commissures

The Anterior Commissure

Structures called commissures in the brain attracted attention in 1992, with public announcements that the anterior commissure, a "cable" of nerve fibres connecting the two sides of the brain, is larger in women and homosexual men than in heterosexual men.[11] (The anterior commissure is unable to be identified in Figure 13, but is to the right of the corpus callosum). But the study also needs verification. The only other study (in 1988) to look at this structure found the opposite: the anterior commissure was significantly larger in men than women. In addition, there was a huge overlap between homosexuals and heterosexuals in the 1992 study (in twenty-seven of a total sample of thirty homosexual men, the size of the anterior commissure fell within the range established for thirty heterosexual men).[1]

The Corpus Callosum

There has also been speculation that part of the corpus callosum in male homosexuals is more like that found in the female brain than in the heterosexual male brain. (The corpus callosum is the largest cable of fibers connecting the two sides of the brain, see Figure 13). There have been twenty-three studies on the corpus callosum—yielding conflicting results. Although the initial study found that the splenium of the corpus callosum was larger and more bulbous in women than in men, none of the other twenty-two studies was able to reproduce the sex difference in size. Some researchers found the splenium more bulbous in men, others in women, and still others found no sex difference. But some of the negative studies were misinterpreted as successful replications.[10] Such conflicting results for gender make nonsense of any attempts to claim male homosexual brains are more like female brains.

Environmental Predominance

The verdict of science on sexual orientation differences in the brain is inconclusive: nothing has been proved. As Vines says in a review of the literature on neuroanatomy and sexual orientation: "Neuroanatomists may yet find themselves handing the search for the roots of homosexuality back to the social psychologists and sociologists."[3]

Certainly there is remarkably little evidence of differences between boys and girls at birth. Boys are 5 percent heavier than girls and 1-2 percent longer, newborn girls have a greater sensitivity to electric shock and react more to a puff of cold air on the skin, but that seems about all. There is little evidence of behavioral differences at birth. Those come later. Boy babies seem readier to crawl away from their mothers, and take longer to come back; by age two, boys and girls react to playblocks in quite a different manner: boys make structures which are taller, girls make ones which are more spread out. But how much of that is from socialization? In chapter three, we mentioned how differently strangers treat even newborn babies once they know what sex they are. As Byne says, "No presumed sexually dimorphic cognitive or behavioral brain function has been shown to be independent of learning and experience."[1]

There is also nothing permanent either about changes to brain microstructure as a result of learning and activity. Measurements of (radioactive) carbon-14 in human brains show that the average carbon atom stays about seven years in brain tissues. This means that the complete material of the brain is changed during a lifetime by substitutions of different atoms and brain cells—even in "permanent" nerve tissue.[12] Nothing is hardwired. Anyone determined to change any behavior should be able to make a substantial difference in thinking and habit patterns within a decade. Biological determinism is a myth.

There are two other brief arguments in favor of an environmentally-based sexuality.

• If only about one quarter of the neurons in the adult brain are present at birth, and the form and structure of the remaining 75 percent that develop depend heavily on learning, experience, exercise and behavior, then there are grounds for arguing that about one quarter of brain structure is biologically fixed and three quarters is the result of environmental interaction. We could argue that because the child experiences so little in the womb in comparison with the bombardment of stimuli he or she begins to receive after birth, the environmental contribution to brain micro-structure is in fact, even at a conservative estimate, much closer to 90 percent. Here we have a very rough approximation of the 90 percent environment and 10 percent biology contributions to sexuality suggested in chapter five, and hinted at again in chapters nine and ten.

• The DNA in all twenty-three pairs of chromosomes in a single fertilized cell is three billion rungs long (see chapter one), but there are 200,000 billion synapses or neuron junctions in the brain. Even if each rung coded for one junction, (which it doesn't, see chapter one) all the rungs together could only specify about one junction in 66,000![13] The rest would have to develop in processes some distance removed from genetic specifications—in other words, under the influence of the wider environment.

Summary

Scientists have not been able to find sexual differences between the brains of boys and girls at birth. They have also found very little difference between male and female brains in adults. Male and female behavior is apparently not hardwired into the brain—let alone homosexuality and heterosexuality. In fact, only one quarter of the brain is formed in a new-born child; the rest is developed through learning and experience (environmental input). We can be confident that whatever male-female differences may be found in adult brains (and, no doubt, more will be at some stage), they will also be largely shaped by learning and behavior. But what learning and experiences do to the brain is not set in concrete either. Brain cells are replaced in roughly seven year cycles, meaning that new neuron pathways can be formed and old ones reshaped. We are not victims of our biology or the experiences which shape the detail of our brain. Anatomy is not destiny; change is always possible.

Notes

1. Byne, W., "Science and Belief: Psychobiological Research on Sexual Orientation," *Journal of Homosexuality* (1995) 30:303-344.

2. LeVay, S., "A difference in hypothalamus structure between heterosexual and homosexual men," *Science* (1991) 253:1034-1037.

3. Vines, G, "Obscure origins of desire," *New Scientist* (28 November 1992) 136:2-8.

4. Shatz, C.J., The Developing Brain, *Scientific American* (March 1992) 26735-41.

5. Kandel, E.R., Hawkins, R.D., "The biological basis of learning and individuality," *Scientific American* (March 1992) 267:53-60.

6. Joseph, S.C., "Current and future trends in AIDS in New York City," *Advances in Alcohol and Substance Abuse* (1987) 7:159-174.

7. Blum, S., "Sex and the single brain," *Current Contents* (1992) 32:6-8.

8. Burr, C., *A Separate Creation* (London: Bantam Books, 1996).

9. Swaab, D.F., Gooren, L.J.G., Hofman, M.A., "Brain research, gender and sexual orientation," *Journal of Homosexuality* (1995) 30:283-301.

10. Byne, W., Parsons, B., "Human sexual orientation. The biologic theories reappraised," *Archives of General Psychiatry* (1993) 50:228-239.

11. Allen, L.S., Gorski, R.A., "Sexual orientation and the size of the anterior commissure in the human brain,"

Proceedings of the National Academy of Sciences (1992) 89:7199-7202.

12. Stenhouse, M.J., Baxter, M.S., "Bomb 14C as a biological tracer," *Nature* (1977) 267:828-832.

13. Koch, C., "Computation and the single neuron," *Nature* (1997) 385:207-210.

Chapter Nine

The Discovery of the "Gay Gene"

In mid-1993, the West was told that a scientist had discovered a "gay gene"—a gene causing homosexuality. The details were confusing for non-scientists, but the headline stuck. For Mr. and Ms. Average Citizen, it seemed that homosexuality might be genetic.

Actually there was no "gay gene." Even the scientist referred to, a gay man, Dr. Hamer of the United States National Institutes of Health, never claimed to have found a gene determining homosexuality. "We have not found the gene—which we don't think exists—for sexual orientation," he said.[1] However, he claimed to have found evidence that some male homosexuality was passed through female members of a family. More specifically, he claimed to have found a linkage between homosexuality in males and a small stretch of the DNA on the X-chromosome.[2]

Gene Linkage Studies

Hamer's work falls into a category of research called "gene linkage studies." There has been a surge of research in this field in the last decade, each success inspiring another. The most spectacular, to date, has been the discovery, early in 1993, of a gene responsible for Huntington's disease. The gene had already been tracked down to chromosome four, but it took six teams of workers at ten different institutions ten years to find whereabouts on chromosome four. Over the last decade, researchers have also identified genes causing cystic fibrosis, muscular dystrophy, and other diseases.

Biologists are also having astonishing success mapping the human genome (more or less on schedule and within budget!), and chromosomal genetic maps densely covered with regions identified by "markers" are now available to researchers in genetics. In the last five years, the genes corresponding to 1450 physical conditions have been identified and their precise location on various chromosomes determined.[3] Inspired by these successes, some scientists began talking optimistically of uncovering the genetic basis to human behaviors in the same way. This is what Hamer tried to do, and what other scientists, called behavioral geneticists, have attempted to do before him, but with scant success. Some gene linkage studies of homosexuality are significantly motivated by a hope that if homosexuality can be shown to be sufficiently linked to biology, it will help erase social stigma.[4-6]

So, research linking human characteristics with genes is back in fashion after decades in the dogbox since the Nazi era.[4]

What Happens in Linkage Studies?

In linkage studies, researchers look for an extended family with an unusually high incidence of some behavior, such as manic depression, and then take samples of tissue from all available members and analyze the DNA, looking for segments in common using sets of tiny, synthesized DNA segments, called "markers"—an identical set for each person. These tiny markers are configured in such a way that they attach in a lock and key fashion to certain stretches of DNA that mirror the markers. Searching for one gene in 100,000 is worse than looking for a contact lens in a swimming pool, but, in this way, similar segments can be found in different people. If the same sequence is associated consistently with a given trait, then researchers assume it lies close to the gene that codes for it or actually is that gene. At that point, a linkage is said to have been shown. In linkage studies a control test is rarely done to see if the segments also appear in those not having the trait.

The strength of linkage analysis is in studying physical diseases that have distinct symptoms and are caused by a single dominant gene. When they attempt to link behaviors to a single gene, they run into a volley of scientific scepticism, for several reasons.

First, no mainstream geneticist believes that behavior is linked to one single gene (see Chapter One). "It's very rare to find genes that have a specific effect," says Harvard biologist Balaban.[4] Plomin, a psychologist at Pennsylvania State University, long active in behavioral genetics and recipient of a grant from the National Institute for Child Health and Human Development to find genes linked to high intelligence, isn't optimistic. At best, he expected to find a gene accounting for a tiny part of variance in intelligence, and his announcement, in November 1997, is consistent with his expectation: he believes he has found a gene accounting for about 2 percent of total variation in IQ. Second, difficulties in diagnosis of some behavioral conditions can create a dubious study group: do they really have the condition or not? The same problem does not arise for physical diseases with clear symptoms. Third, in the word of one writer for *Science,* "the field of behavioral genetics is littered with apparent discoveries that were later called into question or retracted."[7] Let's have a look at some of them.

Manic Depression

Following the dramatic success of linkage studies in the early eighties, workers began looking for DNA segments associated with mental illness. They were highly motivated. The potential payoffs were enormous; manic depression affects about one percent of the world's population. In 1987, there were two announcements: a group from the University of Miami claimed a link between chromosome eleven and manic depression in the Amish population, and a team from Columbia University found a linkage on chromosome X with manic depression in three Israeli families. The media hailed the studies as major breakthroughs, but paid scant attention to the retractions that followed. The Amish study was extended and re-evaluated by a group from the National Institute of Medicine in the U.S.A., who could not find the link, which appeared to be a statistical freak that vanished on closer examination. In 1993, the team from Columbia University withdrew their claim after a closer and more sophisticated look at more Israeli families. They had been mistaken.[4]

Schizophrenia

In 1988, a group from the University College, London Medical School announced in *Nature* that it had found an association of schizophrenia with chromosome five in British and Icelandic families. Coincidentally, in the same issue of *Nature,* a Yale University team reported it could find no such linkage in a study of Swedish families. Although University College defended its research for several years, it finally retracted the results after further research could not reproduce the original findings. "The new families showed no linkage at all," said the leader of the team.[4] Further studies by six groups all suggested chromosome six may be involved—but here again, another two could find no trace! Schizophrenia may well be another case in which many genes are involved, each with a very small contribution. However, even that does not seem likely, because in that case it would probably show up in each generation for four or five generations (see Chapter One). Dr. Balaban, biologist at Harvard University, thinks behavioral genetics is a "hierarchy of worthlessness," with twin studies at the bottom (i.e.. they are somewhat more reliable) and linkage studies of mental illness at the top.[4] It is remarkable to find such strong views about a scientific subject, and he is not a lone voice. Even Kidd, a Yale geneticist who has dedicated his career to searching for genes linked to mental illness, says "there is very little proof that schizophrenia, manic depression and other psychiatric disorders have a genetic origin. Virtually all the evidence supports a genetic explanation, but there are always other explanations."[4]

Violent Crime

A 1960 survey of prison inmates showed an above average proportion of men with an extra Y chromosome. Researchers speculated that since the Y chromosome is the "male" chromosome, these men might be more aggressive and prone to violence. But, although studies found extra-Y men were taller and slightly lower in intelligence, they were otherwise normal. In 1994, the National Academy of Sciences reported there was no evidence to support a link between the extra Y chromosome and violent behavior.[4]

Alcoholism

In 1990, a group from the University of Texas Health Science Centre claimed it had found a genetic marker for alcoholism in a study comparing thirty-five alcoholics with a control group of non-alcoholics. The *New York Times* gave the story front page treatment and hailed the results as a potential watershed in the diagnosis and treatment of alcoholism. The international media also carried the news, and the Texas team came up with a second study which they said confirmed the first. But the popular media made no mention of six other independent studies which could find no association at all. In 1993, the National Institute of Alcohol Abuse and Alcoholism analyzed all the studies in a paper published in the *Journal of the American Medical Association* and declared that the Texas results were anomalous; "We therefore conclude that no physiologically significant association" has been proved, the Institute stated. The leader of

the Institute's team declared the matter "a dead issue."
Another researcher, an advocate of genetic models of
human behavior, remarks of the alleged link: "I think it
is by and large, garbage." As at this writing, the controversy continues, but, obviously, the finding is not easily
replicable.[4]

Hamer's Study

To find the homosexual gene or genes, Hamer and
his colleagues first recruited seventy-six homosexual men,
who identified themselves as predominantly or exclusively homosexual. They found 13.5 percent of their
brothers to be gay, much higher than the 1 percent
incidence of exclusive homosexuality in the general male
population, and also a higher level of homosexuality in
maternal uncles and the sons of maternal aunts. They
then recruited thirty-eight families in which there were
two homosexual brothers, suspecting this would show
more clearly the effect of homosexuality in male relatives on the maternal side. According to Hamer, 20
percent of male relatives were homosexual in this sample.
Hamer then searched for a linkage on the X (female)
chromosome (since males receive their single X chromosome exclusively from their mothers). He postulated, "If
the X chromosome contains a gene that increases the
probability of an individual's being homosexual, then
genetically related gay men should share X chromosome
markers close to that gene."[2] (Actually, it's normal for
about 50 percent of brothers to share a particular sequence, as they will always have their father's Y chromosome, but, on average, half will have one of the mother's
two X chromosomes and half the other. So it's only significant if the percentage of brothers sharing the sequence is well above 50 percent.) Hamer took forty pairs
of gay brothers (thirty-eight from the sibling pairs, two
from the first survey) and analyzed the DNA of the X
chromosome with a series of twenty-two markers.

What did Hamer find? He claimed to have found a "statistically significant correlation" between the homosexual orientation and a genetic sequence on the tip of the long arm of the X chromosome, an area called "Xq28," in thirty-three cases out of the forty. That was 83 percent, well above the chance result of 50 percent. He summarized "We have now produced evidence that one form of male homosexuality is preferentially transmitted through the maternal side and is genetically linked to chromosomal region Xq28."[2] Hamer published his paper in *Science,* in July 1993, and immediately became a controversial figure in the scientific community. Numerous letters to *Nature,* for example, were mostly critical.

Lack of Control Group

Hamer was immediately criticized for his lack of a control group from the general population—a *sine qua non* of any normal scientific study.[6] If the same sequence also appeared consistently in non-gay men, his claim would be void. Nor did he systematically test the heterosexual brothers of the gay men he studied to see if they shared the same sequence, though he did have data from a few heterosexual brothers, some of whom also had the sequence. Hamer replied that basically the whole point of linkage studies was not to examine genetically unrelated populations but genetically related individuals.[8] (In other words, linkage studies are done that way, which is partly why the scientific community does not consider them very reliable.) Heterosexual men could also carry the gene without expressing it, Hamer said. He also argued that the inclusion of heterosexual brothers would have required an "inherently inaccurate" mathematical procedure which "might actually have decreased the accuracy and reliability of our results."[6] But the fact remains—no-one knew if Hamer's piece of "homosexual" DNA was present in the non-gay population. In addition, seven of Hamer's gay pairs did not have the sequence. Hamer put the discordance down to a number of things, including non-genetic factors in homosexuality, or other contributing genetic sequences yet to be discovered.

Inaccurate Statistical Methodology

Two of the strongest criticisms of Hamer's study came from Risch, the scientist who developed the statistical method that Hamer used to calculate the significance of his finding. Hamer claimed his correlation of homosexuality with maternal inheritance was "statistically significant." Risch (Yale University School of Medicine) said there was no statistically significant correlation in part of the work, and unknown significance in the other. "Hamer et al. suggest that their results are consistent with X-linkage because maternal uncles have a higher rate of homosexual orientation than paternal uncles, and cousins related through a maternal aunt have a higher rate than other types of cousins. However, neither of these results is statistically significant."[9] This calculation was redone by another scientist, McGuire at Rutgers University,[10] who said a wrong test had been applied by Hamer to the maternal relatives and, as Risch noted, the result was not statistically significant except for cousins alone, which did not make sense as an inheritance pattern. Secondly, Hamer appeared to say that the odds in favor of his X-chromosome finding being real were 10,000 to 1. Risch said according to the statistical method he had invented and Hamer had used, it was not possible to say. In his reply, Hamer admitted he would welcome help with the interpretation as to what was really significant. A paper published soon after by Lander and Schnork[11] showed that the odds were roughly twenty to one—just significant, according to the standards of most scientists. In other words, even an 83 percent sharing is barely significant (with this sample size). Other aspects of the mathematics appeared shaky, in effect placing the Xq28 region beyond the tip of the chromosome—a physical impossibility. Risch further commented that the alleged X-link could be more apparent than real. "The small sample sizes make these data compatible with a range of possible genetic and environmental hypotheses," he said, and because "so few homosexual men tend to have children, a study of male homosexual orientation will reveal few opportunities for male to male transmission, giving the appearance of an X-linkage."[9]

Shared Sequences Dissimilar

Hamer's paper gives the impression that all sixty-six men from the thirty-three pairs shared an identical sequence within the Xq28 region, but that's not exactly what the study showed. The sequences in any one pair of homosexual brothers were somewhat different from those shared by any other pair of homosexual brothers. In fact, each of thirty-three pairs of brothers shared exactly the same sequence only with his brother. One critic of the paper, Byne, remarks "No single, specific Xq28 sequence (the putative "gay gene") was identified in all sixty-six men."[12] It is possible that the same gene might be found in sequences which are not quite identical, but geneticists are uneasy with the idea.

Hamer and his team used the proper caveats in their paper: they didn't claim determinism, but rather influence and possibilities. They also said their finding needed replicating. But the editor of *Nature,* John Maddox, was clearly concerned the results might have to be retracted. He took the very unusual step of questioning Hamer's findings in an editorial.[13] When asked about this by Hamer in a letter,[14] Maddox replied that "two previous such interpretations (published in this journal) have proved unfounded."[8]

Questionable Ethics

Hamer's work proved controversial, even within his own research team. One young researcher accused Hamer of omitting from the study results that would have made

the findings non-significant. The accusation led to her
dismissal from the research post and a complaint to the
Office of Research Integrity (a U.S. watchdog on scientific ethics), which ruled there was a case to answer[15]—
which could mean Hamer's 83 percent was much too
high. The case faded from view about mid-1997, with no
public resolution. In the meantime, Hamer[16] and colleagues replicated their study using a new population.
This time they called in one of the world's leading genetic statisticians, Fulker, from Colorado. This time, the
results were less impressive—67 percent of homosexual
brothers shared regions rather than 83 percent—and the
odds against it being a freak were again about twenty to
one—just significant. However, they emphasized that the
results applied only to their study group; that is, families
with two homosexual brothers. When a linkage was attempted using homosexual men who had bisexual brothers, a correspondence of only 50 percent was found—no
different from normal genetic sharing between siblings.
A Western Ontario study which attempted to replicate
Hamer's new study also failed perhaps because exclusive
homosexuals and bisexuals were combined for the study.[15]
It showed a 50 percent correspondence, too. As of 1999,
other studies were continuing.

What Does a 67% Concordance Mean?

Leaving aside Hamer's first finding of 83 percent,
let's assume, for the sake of argument, that his second
study is accurate. What does a concordance of 67 percent mean between two homosexual brothers? Sixty seven
percent is 17 percent greater than the 50 percent mark:
a 35 percent increase. For those families with one homosexual and one bisexual, the effect was nil (which may
argue strong environmental influence), and the method
does not give information about those families with just
one homosexual son. How common are families with two
homosexual brothers? We mentioned earlier that Hamer
found 13.5 percent of brothers of homosexuals were also

homosexual. This means that in about one case in seven, there are two homosexual brothers in a family rather than one. For homosexuals as a whole, Hamer's particular genetic effect might affect about five percent (35%/7) of the homosexual population. It is obviously not a very strong effect. More genes could yet be found, and probably will be, but, at this stage, environmental influences could be argued to account for the homosexuality of the other 95 percent. This is consistent with levels of environmental influence suggested by other studies cited in this book (chapters five, eight and ten).

The second paper also showed that families with lesbian sisters did not share a common genetic sequence in the Xq28 region or in other parts of the X-chromosome. If there is some sequence in common, it may show up in a search of other chromosomes.

Probably the track record for linkage studies will improve as researchers take greater care. A recent paper in *Nature Genetics* set down rigorous criteria for linkage studies, arguing that these were essential if the field was to retain any credibility. Using their criteria, Hamer's first study was of borderline significance.[17]

Summary

We can confidently predict half a dozen linkages will be "discovered" between genes and behavior each year. But the important lesson is this: any linkages probably affect only a small proportion of people to a very minor extent. The track record for genetic linkage studies showing a genetic basis to human behavior is so far mediocre. As Gershon, chief of the clinical neurogenetics branch of the National Institute of Mental Health, notes, "There's almost no finding that would be convincing by itself in this field."[4] The controversy will no doubt continue, but most observers will continue to treat claims made by researchers in the field of genetic linkage with great caution. Even a replication becomes meaningless if a third and fourth study cannot find the same effect. Researchers, and particularly statisticians, remain very skeptical.

The scientific community is realizing now that whatever Hamer may have found, it is nothing determinative. As a commentator in the *New Scientist* put it: "Hamer's gene, whatever it turns out to be, is neither necessary nor sufficient to determine homosexual orientation."[18] Hamer himself acknowledges that. To give him the last word: "There will never be a test that will say for certain whether a child will be gay. We know that for certain."[18]

Proponents of the view that homosexuality has psychological and sociological explanations have no difficulty with the possibility of genetic linkages to homosexuality. Any genetic link to a physical characteristic that might heighten a person's sense of gender nonconformity (the strongest known predictor of later homosexuality), could be held to be a contributing factor to later homosexuality. In a boy these might be, for example, genes related to slightness of build, lack of physical co-ordination (making a boy poor at sports), sensitivity. In a girl they might be factors like atypical physical strength, height, or weight.

Notes

1. McKie, R., "The Myth of the Gay Gene," *The Press* (NZ: 30 July 1993): 9.

2. Hamer, D.H., Hu, S., Magnuson, V.L., Hu, N., Pattatucci, A.M.L., "A linkage between DNA markers on the X-chromosome and male sexual orientation," *Science* (1993): 261:321-327.

3. Ellis, N.A., "Ecce Ohno!" *Nature Genetics* (1995): 10:373-375.

4. Horgan, J., "Eugenics revisited," *Scientific American* (June 1993): 268:92-100.

5. Vines, G., "Obscure origins of desire," *New Scientist* (28 November 1992): 136:2-8.

6. Fausto-Sterling, A., Balaban, E., "Genetics and Male Sexual Orientation," *Science* (1993): 261:1257.

7. Pool, R., "Evidence for Homosexuality Gene," *Science* (1993): 261:291-292.

8. Hamer, D., "Sexual orientation," *Nature* (1993): 365:702.

9. Risch, N., Squires-Wheeler, E., Keen, B.J.B., "Male Sexual Orientation and Genetic Evidence," *Nature* (1993): 262:2063-2064.

10. McGuire, T.R., "Is Homosexuality Genetic? A Critical Review and Some Suggestions," *Journal of Homosexuality* (1995): 30:115-145.

11. Lander, E.S., Schork, N.J., "Genetic Dissection of Complex Traits," *Science* (1994): 265:2037-2049.

12. Byne, W., "The Biological Evidence Challenged," *Scientific American* (May 1994): 270:26-31.

13. Maddox, J., "Wilful Public Misunderstanding of Genetics," *Nature* (1993): 364:281.

14. Hamer, D., "Reply," *Nature* (1993): 365:702.

15. Marshall, E., NIH's "Gay Gene study questioned," *Science* (1995): 268:1841.

16. Hu, S., Pattatucci, A.M.L., Patterson, C., Li, L., Fulker, D.W., Cherny, S.S., Kruglyak, L., Hamer, D.L., "Linkage between sexual orientation and chromosome Xq28 in male but not in females," *Nature Genetics* (1995): 11:248-256.

17. Kruglyak, L., "Thresholds and sample sizes," *Nature Genetics* (1996): 14:132-135.

18. Holmes, B., "Gay gene test 'inaccurate and immoral,' " *New Scientist* (5 March 1994): 141:9.

Chapter Ten

What if I'm an Identical Twin?

Over the last decade half a dozen studies of twins who are genetically identical have found that where one twin is homosexual, the identical co-twin is also homosexual in about 50 percent of cases. Although the results have been variable, taken as a whole the studies would appear to give support to the idea that homosexuality has some genetic basis. Let's have a closer look at twin studies.

What are twin studies?

Twin studies are a method of estimating the relative contributions of genetics, shared family environment, and unique individual experiences in the development of any trait. They have been applied to hundreds of traits, including IQ, extroversion, neuroticism, and, of course, sexual orientation. Researchers in the field use statistical formulae to put a number on the relative contributions of genetics and environment. Though twin study methodology has been constantly refined over the last sixty years, the results of twin studies have come under intense scrutiny, criticism, and sometimes vigorous condemnation from other scientists. Feeling rather beleaguered, those who specialize in twin studies have often been satisfied with establishing that there was a real, though small, genetic influence.

Twin studies compare identical twins (who have identical genes) with non-identical twins (who, on average, share 50 percent of their genes). They take advantage of the situation where each twin of a pair shares the same family environment. For each group of twins (identical and non-identical), the fraction of pairs sharing the trait is recorded and used to calculate a statistic called the "tetrachloric correlation coefficient," symbolized by the letter "r," which ranges from 0 for no concordance (that is, the trait is not shared with any co-twin in that group) to 1 for a perfect positive concordance (the trait is shared by all co-twins in that group). This leads to the statistic r_{MZ} for identical twins and r_{DZ} for fraternal twins. (MZ stands for monozygotic twins—from one ovum; DZ for dizygotic twins—from two separate ova). These are fed into the following simple formulae, which calculate the respective contributions of genes, shared environment and unique experiences. Thus:

Genetic influence ("heritability"); $h^2 = 2(r_{MZ} - r_{DZ})$
Shared environment; $c^2 = 2r_{DZ} - r_{MZ}$
Unique experiences; $e^2 = 1 - r_{MZ}$

The "unique experience" category also includes any fuzzy areas in the measurement of the trait (e.g., whether this person really has a certain condition or not).

There were six significant male twin studies of homosexuality published up to 1995, and they came up with much the same figure. After the math has been done, about 50 percent of the total contribution to male sexual orientation appears to be "heritable."[1-6] However one study,[3] only found 20 percent "heritability." More about heritability later in the chapter.

The Rules of Twin Study Analysis

For the findings of a twin study to hold, the population under study has to conform to the following seven rules or assumptions. If it doesn't, the findings will be astray from a mild to severe extent. For twin studies to be accurate in their conclusions about homosexuality, it would have to be shown that:

1. The identical homosexual twins did not volunteer for the study at higher rates than fraternal homosexual twins.

2. Families really do treat each of a pair of twins identically (the "shared environments" assumption).

3. Homosexuality has a statistically "normal" distribution in the population.

4. There is no interaction between genes and environment.

5. People with the "homosexual gene" very rarely mate with others carrying the "homosexual gene."

6. The twins do not imitate each other—particularly, identical twins, do not encourage each other to be homosexual.

7. The twins, apart from being twins, are very similar to the rest of the population (e.g., in physical characteristics and in incidence). By incidence we mean that because about one percent of the population is exclusively homosexual, about one percent of people who are one of a twin pair should also be exclusively homosexual.

Are These Rules Broken?

Unfortunately, most of these assumptions are violated—some more than others—in most twin studies of homosexuals, and the net effect is a drop in the genetic contribution to something possibly as low as 10 percent.

Let's look at them.

1. Twin studies on homosexuality get most of their subjects from the gay community. "Volunteer error" is a well-known phenomenon in surveys. People with a condition under study are curious about it and volunteer at higher rates than the average person, especially if they are twins, and particularly if they are identical twins, who have a closer than normal bond. This kind of error in twin studies artificially increases the apparent genetic influence. (For a fuller discussion of this effect see the section entitled Lesbianism, later in this chapter)

2. Do families treat twins the same? Parents may claim they are utterly fair and even-handed and treat all their children the same way, but in fact they tend to respond to their children according to their differently expressed psychological needs. Although this is usually not consciously planned, it amounts to a strongly individualized care that can be experienced as quite different than that given to another sibling. Thus, non-identical twins may be treated quite differently than one another, contrary to the assumption of twin studies that they are treated identically. For example, it is known that mothers of non-identical twins treat them with differing warmth, but treat identical twins almost the same.[7,8] If, for argument, different parental treatment of fraternal twins contributed to a "defensive detachment" (of the kind discussed in chapter three) by a "disadvantaged" co-twin, twin study methodology would lower r_{DZ} and artificially inflate the heritability (see the "heritability" formula above). In other words, twin studies could interpret an environmental factor as a genetic factor. Byne and Parsons[9] comment that although the equal environments assumption might hold true for intelligence and certain personality traits, sexual orientation appears to be "significantly influenced by more idiosyncratic aspects of the (family) environment."

3. Homosexuality certainly does not have a normal distribution in the population. It has what statisticians call a "positively skewed distribution" (Figure 15). Most surveys of homosexual incidence show about 1 percent of the population is exclusively homosexual, a few surveys give lower figures, and quite a few give slightly higher percentages.* The positively skewed distribution tends to give higher values for both correlation coefficients, giving a bigger difference between them, thus exaggerating the genetic contribution.

---

* Although a range of surveys seems an irregular way to calculate the shape of a distribution, it is an acceptable statistical method.

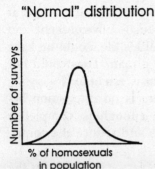
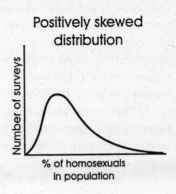

Figure 15:

4. Is there interaction between effects produced by genes and the environment? Of course there is. That is almost a definition of a living organism. Probably the most important criticism that has been levelled at twin studies is that they treat nature and nurture as totally separate variables that don't interact during human development. If interaction does occur between the genes and the environment in any population under investigation in a twin study, it has the effect of artificially raising the "heritability."[8, 10, 11] Researchers call the hypothetical non-interaction of nature and nurture the "additive" model, are generally critical of it, and thus, by implication, skeptical about twin studies. "In a specific practical situation, do we really believe that the additive model is at all realistic? The answer is No," says one statistician, Goodall.[12] One set of researchers[13] who looked for gene-environment interactions (not in a study of sexual orientation) found eleven. So, these interactions certainly exist.

Let's look at an example. If a person were genetically inclined to become homosexual, would an environ-

ment which encouraged him to express his sexuality (e.g.,
homosexual porn, or advances from homosexual men),
have no effect on him whatsoever? Of course it would. If
he were brought up in an all-female environment and
completely isolated from men all his life, could he have
a homosexual relationship with a man? How could he?
An environment containing men is essential.

Is this assumption that there is no interaction between genes and environment enough to completely
destroy the value of twin studies and reduce the contribution of genes to zero?

No, it's not. But it is another factor that reduces the
calculated genetic contribution slightly, though not to
zero. Genuine efforts have been made to check for interaction between genes and environment in some twin
studies and to factor it into the results, because statisticians know that the genetic component might be exaggerated in a method based on no interaction. But the
checks were inadequate—not because the method was
faulty, but because the sample sizes weren't large
enough.[12] (On smaller samples the checks were simply
too insensitive and the results were erratic—some samples
showing high interaction, some low, but usually showing
little interaction.[14]) Really large samples of twins have
only become available recently. It is fair to say that when
interaction has been adequately checked in large samples,
it has usually been found, but it does not overwhelmingly
lower the genetic contribution.[8, 11]

5. Do people with the "homosexual gene" or genes
tend to marry each other more frequently than they
marry those without the gene or genes? This is a completely hypothetical question. Even if such a gene or
genes existed, we would have no way of knowing whether
such people marry each other more frequently. If they
do, the mathematical formulae used in twin studies would
have the effect of reducing the genetic factor too far—an
opposite effect to all the other factors mentioned here.[15]

6. Do twins tend to imitate each other in homosexual development? Twins certainly do imitate each other (e.g., in antisocial behavior, in truthfulness or lying).[8] It is quite conceivable that the same might happen in the development of homosexuality. Twins often have an unusually close bond, sharing intimately and supporting each other, particularly if they are identical twins. These environmental factors could lead to higher levels of homosexuality in identical twins, making the genetic content appear higher. To discover if imitation might be artificially raising the heritability figures, researchers checked to see if the correlation for the identical twins was more than double that for fraternal twins[6]—the statistical indicator of inflated heritability. In many cases, (particularly for females) it was.

7. Perhaps most importantly, it is very doubtful twins are similar to the general population. They start life smaller on average than other babies, and have fewer verbal and social skills till as late as eight years.[16] The rate of child abuse among twins is nearly three times higher than for the general population.[17] They tend to be found toward the bottom of the social scale and are often subject to harassment and teasing by schoolmates. Young male twins are often called "fairies," a common identifying mark of childhood gender non-conformity, one of the strongest predictors of later homosexuality.[18] Twins are such good and sufficient friends to each other that their individuality and sexuality may not be entirely developed. For example, they are significantly more often unmarried than singletons (33-40 percent of male twins may remain unmarried, and 22.5-26 percent of female twins—rates which may be about double those in the rest of the population, though this effect was not found in the Australian twin study). They are thus a suspect population for a sexual survey.[13]

Perhaps most critically, there is a higher rate of homosexuality in identical twins than in the rest of the

population. Results of four studies combined[19-22] show
that 3.8 percent of twins are exclusively homosexual,
compared with 0.9 percent in the general population,
that is, about four times higher. By this we mean that at
least one member of an identical twin pair was exclusively homosexual in 3.8 percent of cases. This effect is
very high, and could be either an indicator of a large
volunteer error, an unusually urban-based sample, or
some unusual psychodynamic effect, but would certainly
exaggerate heritability once again.

How Much Does the Genetic Factor Fall?

Homosexuality, by and large, falls outside the rules
of twin study analysis. In most studies of homosexual
populations, most of the assumptions that must be met
if the results are to be trusted have been violated, and in
such a way that heritability is significantly over-exagger-
ated. Does this mean that twin studies are an inappro-
priate tool for gauging the genetic content of sexual
orientation? At this stage, we can only judge by looking
at much more sophisticated studies of other traits which
have been investigated most closely for the effects of
violated assumptions.[8, 11] In general, they find that the
critics have a partial point: the genetic proportion gets
eroded, but is still real. So it is a good bet that the 50
percent heritability figure for male sexual orientation is
quite a bit too high. How much might it fall? We don't
know, but it is not out of the question that, even for
males, it could ultimately fall to about 10 percent, as one
of the most definitive studies on lesbians has found. (See
next section.) Because twin studies so easily exaggerate
the genetic contribution, it is much more likely that a
study showing a lower heritability is closer to the mark.

Lesbianism

Twin studies of lesbians have tended to show a low
genetic contribution. The first,[20] which was very small,

Eckert et al. (1986), found four twin pairs who had been brought up separated at birth. They were discordant for homosexuality, suggesting the heritability was low. King and McDonald,[3] published a study in 1993 examining the heritability of homosexuality in a study of thirty-eight male pairs and eight female pairs. They suggested that the heritability for both was quite low, implying that the heritability of lesbianism itself was low. Another study in 1993 by Whitam et al.[2] of four female identical twin pairs found three of them were concordant for lesbianism. This suggested a possible genetic influence, but the study was very small.

The first really large study, published in 1993, by Bailey et al.,[6] showed that of seventy-one sets of identical twins, one of each of which was lesbian, 48 percent of co-twins were bisexual or lesbian, and of thirty-seven sets of non-identical twins, 16 percent of co-twins were bisexual or lesbian. This calculated out at between 40 percent and 76 percent heritability for lesbianism, depending on assumptions. The researchers were fully aware that their sample of lesbians, gathered by advertisement, might be biased, but the genetic contribution was so high that it seemed unlikely the bias was significant.

Twin Register Studies

Two more recent studies (Hershberger[59] and unpublished Australian work by Martin and Bailey) used existing twin registers, which should have lowered any volunteer bias, but throw the results for both homosexuality and lesbianism into confusion. The former found 55% heritability for lesbianism and zero for male homosexuality, the latter, zero heritability for lesbianism and 40% heritability for men. These contradict each other and the previous studies. (Hershberger also found that MZ twins stongly influence each other and that the heritability of heterosexual attraction was only 18%).

The best estimate of the genetic component of lesbianism is so imprecise that it may be consistent either
with zero or 50%, and hence consistent with genetic levels suggested by the data discussed in other chapters
five, eight, and nine, which maintained that environmental influences easily predominate.

Meaning of a 50% Heritability

Let's be very generous and grant that the genetic
proportion might be 50 percent. What does that mean?
Does 50 percent heritability dictate behavior anyway?

Few studies of behavior actually report heritability of
more than 50 percent for any trait, but many are around
the 50 percent mark. The following table is from the
published literature on twins, and gives you some idea of
the range of behaviors (and a few medical conditions)
subjected to twin study analysis. There have been multiple twin studies on some characteristics, but we will
quote only one randomly selected result from each.

Characteristic Studied	Heritability Found (often ±20%)
Smoking	0%[24]
Hostility	0%[25]
Cynicism	0%[25]
Paranoid alienation	0%[25]
Obsessive-compulsive disorder	0%[26]
Narcissism	0%[26]
Anxiety	20%[27]
Attitude to family	24%[28]
Schizophrenia	28%[29]
Multiple sclerosis	28%[29]
Fertility	30%[30]
Neurosis	36%[27]
Psychosis	39%[31]
Lying	43%[31]

Anorexia nervosa	44%[32, 33]
Fear of the unknown	46%[34]
Psychological inpatient care	47%[35]
Extroversion	50%[36, 31]
Depression	50%[23]
Criminality	50-60%[37, 38]
Alcoholism	0-60%[39]
Altruism	50%[40]
Religiosity	50%[41]
Fundamentalism	50%[15]
Homosexuality (male)	50%[1]
Divorce	52%[42,43]
Self realization	58%[44]
Racial prejudice/bigotry	70%[45]
Dyslexia	76%[38]
Height	90%[46]
Phenylketonuria‡	100%[39]

Obviously, even for something as greatly inherited as height, there is still some environmental effect. For example, a child fed a poor, protein deficient diet will not grow as tall as one who regularly eats steaks.

But even if heritability is about 50 percent, does it mean that a behavior or personality is forced on a person to that extent? Let's look at a few other twin studies that have come up with a heritability roughly similar to Bailey and Pillard's 50 percent for homosexuality, and see how far that 50 percent figure actually determines a behavior. A few in this category are divorce, depression, altruism, criminality, religiosity, fundamentalism, psychological inpatient care, fear of the unknown, and perhaps alcoholism. We know enough about some of these to

---

‡Phenylketonuria is not a behavioral trait. It is an enzyme deficiency 100% genetically caused. It was included in the table to show the contrast between a genuine genetic condition and a behavioral trait.

know that divorce, alcoholism, religiosity, criminal behavior, and inpatient care are not genetically destined.
The authors of the paper which found such a high heritability for divorce were apologetic. Obviously, they remarked with some embarrassment, divorce does depend
on another person.

So it mightn't be easy, but with help, some of these
traits that are apparently half inherited—even religiosity!—can be avoided. Significant intervention might be
required for a long time, but Alcoholics Anonymous,
Prison Fellowship, Marriage Guidance, and numerous
support groups show that nothing is inevitable in these
categories. Why should homosexuality be any different?

Even if "heritability" is as high as researchers al-
lege—and there are many reasons why it almost certainly
isn't—homosexuality is not destined.

No Genetic Determinism

• Firstly, even a 50 percent heritability means that
homosexuality is not genetically determined. If it were,
then all the identical co-twins would also be homosexual
since they are genetically identical. It also means that
homosexuality is not environmentally determined either.
If it were, then all the identical co-twins would also be
homosexual, since their environment is identical. According to twin studies, no-one is a powerless victim of
his or her genes or environment.

• Secondly, the co-twins who were homosexual did
not follow the kind of distribution typical of a genetically
determined trait. (Here you will need to refresh your
memory of the Kinsey Scale, chapter two, Figures 8 and
9.) If individual twins in a group of twin pairs are class
six on the Kinsey scale, and genetic influences are particularly important, you would expect their co-twins to
also be mostly six, with some fives, fewer fours and so on.
Instead, co-twins are either strongly five or six, or else
zero or one, with virtually nothing between. This clear
polarization also argues for a very strong environmental,

rather than genetic, effect. It could also be argued that there was very strong volunteering of pairs of twins who were exclusively, or nearly exclusively, homosexual—a violation of assumption one.

• Byne and Parsons [9] raise a third difficulty, particularly with a study of male homosexuals by Bailey and Pillard in 1991. If homosexuality were genetic, fraternal twins and non-twin biological brothers, who both have about half their genes in common, should be roughly equivalent for concordance. That is, they would show about the same levels of "genetic" homosexuality. But they don't. Bailey and Pillard found a concordance between identical twins of 52 percent; fraternal twins, 22 percent; non-twin biological brothers, 9.2 percent; and adopted brothers 11 percent (the latter very high compared with the expected few percent for the population as a whole). "This is at odds with a simple genetic hypothesis," say Byne and Parsons.

• Fourthly, and very importantly, a 50 percent heritability does not mean that homosexuality is 50 percent inherited. "Heritability," the term the behavioral geneticists have chosen to represent the genetic factor, is one of the most misleading names they could have chosen because homosexuality is mostly not inherited. That is, only about eight percent of the sons of homosexual fathers are also homosexual.[47, 48]

Heritability in the twin study context is a word that is used to represent the influence of genes in relation to environmental influences at one very specific place and time in history. In twin studies, heritability is something which rises and falls inversely to the environmental contribution. That is, if opposite-effect environmental influences are brought to bear, the genetic contribution drops commensurately. Heritability is a function of what is true, on average, at the time of the study in particular social conditions. For example, twin studies in Australia showed a genetic contribution to tonsillectomy which varied with time, depending particularly on one environmental factor: whether or not tonsillectomy was medically fashionable.[49] If it was, the environmental contribution increased, and the genetic factor fell.

It is possible to deliberately increase the strength of genetic influences. You simply ride along with them, encourage and practice them. There are some fascinating Swedish and other studies on twins[50-54] which show that genetic influences, particularly on mental processes, increase with age, right up to age eighty. How does that happen? When children are young, the environmental influences—instruction, controls on behavior—are strongest. In adulthood more personal autonomy allows relaxation of some of the rules, so the genetic factor increases slightly in importance. In old age, people with far fewer pressures on them revert to what comes easily; they can please themselves more, relax. They can let the genetic influences predominate, or even encourage them. Many with disciplined habits will maintain a strong "environmental" influence on themselves, but, at least in some Western countries, on average, the contribution of genetic influences increases with age. Other studies showed that genetic influences on children of school age diminished in highly-regulated households, but in households where the children were less restrained, the genetic influence was stronger.[55-57]

Genetic contribution to certain traits can vary from country to country and time to time. For example, the heritability of height, which is 90 percent in the west, is far lower in Egypt, where family influences are far more important.[58] That is, in the West, where food is plentiful, people can reach their full genetic height. But in some third world countries, the height a person grows may depend on the way limited food is shared round the family (some cultures preferentially feed boys, or oldest boys). Changes in social mores and increasing availability of food can swing the balance back toward a genetic predominance.

Summary

Homosexuality is not genetically determined. If it were, identical twins would show 100% concordance for the trait and no twin study on any behavioral trait has come remotely near that figure. Twin studies on homosexuality in males have come up with a maximum figure of 50 percent 'heritability,' but in so doing they break many of the statistical rules protecting the validity of twin studies results. Overall, these violations decrease the genetic content of homosexuality to well below the 50 percent mark, and possibly to something as low as 10 percent. The conflicts between the various studies are disquieting. And don't forget what heritability means. It is not a measure of how much a trait is inherited. It is, more accurately, a measure of the balance between environment and genetic input into a trait at any one place at a point in time. Heritability is something that rises and falls in direct response to the amount of environmental intervention. An opposite environmental influence can reduce a genetic effect to something negligible.

But even if, for the sake of argument, we accept the 50 percent level as correct, comparison with other traits showing genetic influences of comparable strength makes it clear that homosexuality is not determined

Ultimately, it doesn't matter much whether the genetic contribution is large or small. It doesn't determine our behavior in any way. Any genetic influence can be counteracted with an opposite environmental influence, and an environmental influence can be counteracted with an opposite environmental influence. We are not the victims of our personal histories either.

The battle is not really at the level of our genes. It's at the level of our choices.

Notes

1. Bailey, J.M., Pillard, R.C., "A genetic study of male sexual orientation," *Archives of General Psychiatry* (1991): 48:1089-1096.

2. Whitam, F.L., Diamond, M., Martin, J., "Homosexual orientation in twins—a report of 61 pairs and 3 triplet sets," *Archives of Sexual Behavior* (1993): 22:187-206.

3. King, M., McDonald, E., "Homosexuals who are twins. A study of 46 probands," *British Journal of Psychiatry* (1992): 160:407-409.

4. Buhrich, N., Bailey, J.M., Martin, N.G., "Sexual orientation, sexual identity, and sex-dimorphic behaviors in male twins," *Behavior Genetics* (1991): 21:75-96.

5. Holden, C., "More on Genes and Homosexuality," *Science* (1995): 268:1571.

6. Bailey, J.M., Pillard, R.C., Neale, M.C., Agyei, Y., "Heritable factors influence sexual orientation in women," *Archives of General Psychiatry* (1993): 50:217-223.

7. Graham, P.J., Stevenson, J., "A twin study of genetic influences on behavioral deviance," *Journal of the American Academy of Child Psychiatry* (1985): 24:33-41.

8. Eaves, L.J., Last, K.A., Young, D.A., Martin, N.G., "Model fitting approaches to the analysis of human behavior," *Heredity* (1978): 41:249-320.

9. Byne, W., Parsons, B., "Human sexual orientation. The biologic theories reappraised," *Archives of General Psychiatry* (1993): 50:228-239.

10. Lathrope, G.M., Lalouel, J.M., Jacquard, A., "Path analysis of family resemblance and gene-environment interaction," *Biometrics* (1984): 40:611-625.

11. Eaves, L.J., Eysenck, H.J., Martin, N.G., *Social Attitudes: A Model of Cultural Inheritance* (London: Academic Press, 1989).

12. Wahlsten, D., "Insensitivity of the analysis of variance to heredity-environment interaction," *Behavioral and Brain Science* (1990): 13:109-161.

13. Heath, A.C., Jardine, R., Martin, N.G., "Interactive effects of genotype and social environment in alcohol consumption in female twins," *Journal of the Study of Alcoholism* (1989): 50:38-48.

14. Truett, K.R., Eaves, L.J., Walters, E.E., Heath, A.C., Hewitt, J.K., Meyer, J.M., Silberg, J., Neale, M.C., Martin, N.G., Kendler, K.S., "A model system for analysis of family resemblance in extended kinships of twins," *Behavior Genetics* (1994): 24:35-49.

15. Waller, N.G., Kojetin, B.A., Bouchard, T.J., Lykken, D.T., Tellegen, A., "Genetic and environmental influences on religious interests, attitudes and values: a study of twins reared apart and together," *Psychological Science* (1990): 1:138-142.

16. Powers, W.F., Kiely, J.L., "The risks confronting twins. A national perspective," *American Journal of Obstetrics and Gynecology* (1995): 170:456-461.

17. Nelson, H.B., Martin, C.A., "Increased child abuse in twins," *Child Abuse and Neglect* (1985): 9:501-505.

18. Winestone, M.C., "Twinning and Psychological Differentiation," In *The Child and His Family* edited by E.J. Anthony and C. Chiland (New York: John Wiley, 1976), 119-132.

19. Buhrich, N., Loke, C., "Homosexuality, suicide and parricide in Australia," *Journal of Homosexuality* (1989): 15:113-129.

20. Eckert, E.D., Bouchard, T.J., Bohlen, J., Heston, L.L., "Homosexuality in Monozygotic Twins reared apart," *British Journal of Psychiatry* (1986): 148:421-425.

21. Koch, G., "Die bedeutinggenetischer faktoren für das menschliche verhalten," *Arzliche Praxis* (1965): 17:823, 839-846.

22. Heston, L.L., Shields, J., "Homosexuality in twins," *Archives of General Psychiatry* (1968): 18:149-160.

23. Walters, E.E., Neale, M.C., Eaves, L.J., Heath, A.C., Kessler, R.C., Kendler, K.S., "Bulimia nervosa and major depression. A study of common genetic and environmental factors," *Psychological Medicine* (1992): 22:617-622.

24. Swan, G.E., Carmelli, D., Rosenman, R.H., "Psychological characteristics in twins discordant for smoking behavior: a matched-twin-pair analysis," *Addictive Behaviors* (1988): 13:51-60.

25. Cormelli, D., Rosenman, R.H., Swan, G.E., "The Cook and Medley HO scale: a heritability analysis in adult male twins," *Psychosomatic Medicine* (1988): 50:165-174.

26. Dahl, A.A., "The personality disorders: a critical review of family, twin, and adoption studies," *Journal of Personality Disorders* (1993): 7:86-99.

27. Tambs, K., Moum, T., "Low genetic effect and age-specific family effect for symptoms of anxiety and depression in nuclear families, half-sibs and twins," *Journal of Affective Disorders* (1993): 27:183-195.

28. Plomin, R., McClearn, G.E., Pedersen, N.L., Nesselroade, J.R., Bergeman, C.S., "Genetic influence on adults' rating of their current family environment," *Journal of Marriage and the Family* (1989): 51:791-803.

29. Torrey, E.F., "Are we overestimating the genetic contribution to schizophrenia?" *Schizophrenia Bulletin* (1992): 18:159-170.

30. Lykken, D.T., Bouchard, T.J., Jr., McGue, M., Tellegen, A., "The Minnesota twin family registry: some initial findings," *Acta Geneticae Medicae Gemellologicae Roma* (1990): 39:35-70.

31. Tambs, K., Sundet, J.M., Eaves, L., Solaas, M.H., Berg, K., "Pedigree analysis of Eysenck personality questionnaire (EPW) scores in monozygotic (MZ) twin families," *Behavioral Genetics* (1991): 21:369-382.

32. Nigel, K.L., Jones, K.H., "Predisposition factors in anorexia nervosa," *Adolescence* (1992): 27:381-386.

33. Rutherford, J., McGriffin, P., Katz, R.J., Murray, R.M., "Genetic influences on eating attitudes in a normal female twin population," *Psychological Medicine* (1993): 23:425-436.

34. Stevenson, J., Batten, N., Cherner, M., "Fears and fearfulness in children and adolescents: a genetic analysis of twin data," *Journal of Child Psychology and Psychiatry* (1992): 33:977-985.

35. Allgulander, C., Nowak, J., Rice, J.P., "Psychopathology and treatment of 30, 344 twins in Sweden. II. Heritability estimates of psychiatric diagnosis and treatment in 12884 twin pairs," *Acta Psychiatrica Scandinavica* (1991): 83:12-15.

36. Robinson, J.L., Kagan, J., Reznick, J.S., Corley, R., "The heritability of inhibited and uninhibited behavior: a twin study," *Developmental Psychology* (1992): 28:1030-1037.

37. Eysenck, H.J., "Genetic and environmental contributions to individual differences in the three major dimensions of personality," *Journal of Personality* (1990): 58:245-261.

38. Gottesman, I.I., Carey, G., "Extracting meaning and direction from twin data," *Psychiatric Developments* (1993): 1:35-50.

39. Horgan, J., (1993): "Eugenics revisited," *Scientific American* (June 1993): 268:92-100.

40. Rushton, J.P., Fulker, D.W., Neale, M.C., Blizard, R.A., Eysenck, H.J., Altruism and genetics, *Acta Geneticae Medicae Gemellologicae Roma* (1984): 33:265-271.

41. Bouchard, T.J., Lykken, D.T., McGue, M., Segal, N.L., Tellegen, A., "Sources of human psychological differences: the Minnesota study of twins reared apart," *Science* (1990): 250:223-228.

42. Holden, C., "Why divorce runs in families," *Science* (1992): 258:1734.

43. McGue, M., Lykken, D.T., "Genetic influence on risk of divorce," *Psychological Science* (1992): 3:368-373.

44. Gough, H.G., "Genetic and environmental variation on the California Psychological Inventory vector scales," *Journal of Personality Assessment* (1990): 54:463-468.

45. Loehlin, J.C., "Nature, nurture and conservatism in the Australian twin study," *Behavior Genetics* (1993): 23:287-290.

46. Plomin, R., "The Role of Inheritance in Behavior," *Science* (1990): 248:183-188.

47. Bailey, J.M., Bobrow, D., Wolfe, M., Mikach, S.M., "Sexual orientation of adult sons of gay fathers," *Developmental Psychology* (1995): 31:124-129.

48. Patterson, C.J., "Children of lesbian and gay parents," *Child Development* (1992): 63:1025-1042.

49. Martin, N.G., Kehren, U., Battistutta, D., Mathews, J.D., "Iatrogenic influences on the heritability of childhood tonsillectomy: cohort differences in twin concordance," *Acta Geneticae Medicae Gemellologicae Roma* (1991): 40:165-172.

50. Torgerson, A.M., "Longitudinal research on temperament in twins. Increase in genetic contribution with age," *Acta Geneticae Medicae Gemellologiae Roma* (1987): 36:145-154.

51. Harris, J.R., "Age differences," *Journals of Gerontology* (1992): 47:213-220.

52. Wilson, R.S., "The Louisville twin study: developmental synchronies in behavior," *Child Development* (1983): 54:296-316.

53. Torgeson, A.M., "Longitudinal research on temperament in twins," *Acta Geneticae Medicae Gemellologiae Roma* (1987): 36:145-154.

54. McClearn, G.E., Johansson, B., Berg, S., Pedersen, N.L., Ahern, F., Petrill, S.A., Plomin, R., "Substantial genetic influence on cognitive abilities in twins 80 or more years old," *Science* 276 (1997): 1560-1563.

55. Fischbein, S., Guttman, R., Nathan, M., Esrachi, A., "Permissiveness-restrictiveness for twins and the Israeli Kibbutz," *Acta Geneticae Medicae Gemellologiae Roma* (1990): 39:245-257.

56. Fischbein, S., Guttman, R., "Twins' perception of their environment: a cross-cultural comparison of changes over time," *Acta Geneticae Medicae Gemellologiae Roma* (1992): 41:275-286.

57. Akerman, B.A., Fischbein, S., "Within-pair similarity in MZ and DZ twins from birth to eighteen years of age," *Acta Geneticae Medicae Gemellologiae Roma* (1992): 41:155-164.

58. Abdel-Rahim, A.R., Nagoshi, C.T., Vandenberg, S.G., "Twin resemblance in cognitive ability in an Egyptian sample," *Behavior Genetics* (1990): 20:33-43.

59. Hershberger, S.L., "A twin registry study of male and female sexual orientation," *The Journal of Sex Research* (1997): 34:212-222.

Chapter Eleven

Path Analysis:
Where Does it Lead?

Another method that has been used in debate about the origins of homosexuality is a statistical tool called path analysis. As you might expect, path analysis tries to identify the most common path or paths leading to a particular condition, such as cancer. Path analysis produces a diagram (see Figures 16 and 17) which visually demonstrates the network of causes and attempts to assign a relative importance to each cause. The method works best when there are a relatively small number of causes.

Two studies of homosexuality have been attempted using this method; one by a team, Bell, Weinberg and Hammersmith, using data gathered in 1969-70,[1] and another by Van Wyk and Geist in 1984,[2] using male and female data collected by Dr. Kinsey in the forties, but corrected for bias.

Bell et al., designed a list of questions intended to test current sociological and psychological theories about the causes of homosexuality and provide information about the categories, called "variables," that appear in capital letters in Figures 16 and 17. For example, the question, "During the time you were growing up how afraid were you of your father? Very much, somewhat, very little, not at all," provided information for the variable "negative relationship with father," in Figure 16. Some questions were open-ended questions, such as "How

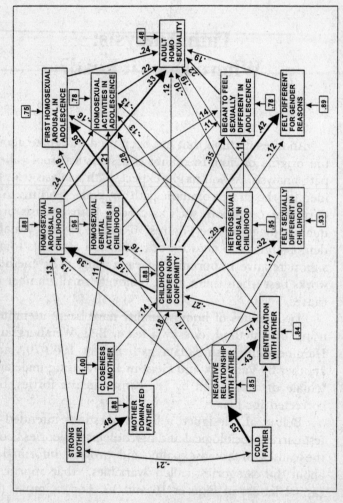

Figure 16: Path Analysis: Male Homosexuality

The path analyses (Figures 16 and 17) have been used to argue that homosexuality has no familial or social causes. In fact they show a good level of support for psychological models. Experts in path analysis agree that the strongest paths shown in these figures (see, also, text) are significant.

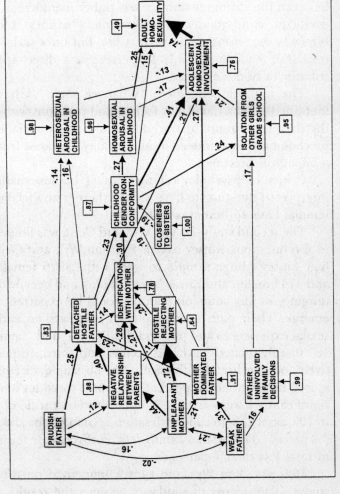

Figure 17: Path Analysis: Lesbianism

did you feel about dating?" When all the answers were in, the team used a complex statistical procedure to see which of the different variables were most common and attempted to link them into a causal pathway.

Some paths showed up more strongly than others, but even the strongest variable was rather mediocre as a predictor; child gender non-conformity ("sissiness") for boys was the strongest single variable. But on a scale of 0 to 100, it measured only 12 percent as a direct contributor to homosexuality.

The authors concluded: "What we seem to have identified . . . is a pattern of feeling and reactions within the child that cannot be traced back to a single social or psychological root; indeed homosexuality may arise from a biological precursor."

Critics of psychological theories of homosexuality interpreted the study to have proved there is no social or familial basis to homosexuality.[3]

The second study, by Van Wyk and Geist, was limited to the questions Kinsey asked. But Van Wyk and Geist had Kinsey's huge sample to work with: 3526 females and 4143 males, and Kinsey's questioning had been wide ranging, so any common features could be expected to emerge. Their path analysis put an emphasis on early sexual experiences and put "gender related" and "familial" (family-related) variables second and third, respectively, on the list of influences. But no single variable scored higher than 10 percent, and most variables were significantly lower—around 3.6 percent. On a scale of 0 to 100, poor relationship with father accounted for about 3.9 percent. For females, family related effects were found to total less than 1 percent.

However, Van Wyk and Geist commented on their study: "The degree of similarity between the results of this study and that of Bell et al. . . . is striking. In each case sexual experience variables accounted for the most . . . [adult homosexuality] followed by gender-related variables and family-related variables in that order."[2]

The research community was puzzled by the results of the two studies, because social factors did not clearly predominate. The studies were fuel to those who rejected an environmental explanation and sought a genetic or biological one. So what was going on? Let's look in more detail at the studies.

Bell et al.

Male homosexuality

Bell et al. actually discovered a number of paths to male homosexuality (see Figure 16), and the three most common lend support to psychological theories suggested in chapter three (cold father, negative relationship with father, negative identification with father, childhood gender non-conformity, homosexual arousal in childhood or first homosexual experience in adolescence, adult homosexuality). Childhood gender nonconformity was made up of three factors: how much boys disliked typical boys' activities, how much they enjoyed typical girls' activities, and how "masculine" or "feminine" adult homosexuals said they had felt growing up.

Bell et al. comment, "childhood gender non-conformity turns out to be a very strong predictor of adult sexual preference among the males in our sample. With total effects of 0.61 (on a scale of 0 to 1) it ranks first in importance among our 15 developmental variables and appears to influence a variety of explicitly sexual variables; in fact it has a direct connection to every single variable following it on the path model." They go on to outline the path, remarking that boys who did not conform to the childhood gender stereotype were more likely to "feel sexually different," either in childhood or adolescence; more likely to experience "homosexual arousal" in childhood or adolescence; somewhat more likely to have some kind of "homosexual genital activities in childhood;" and more extensive involvement in "homosexual activities in adolescence." "Each of these [variables] in turn makes adult homosexuality more probable."

Lesbianism

In women, the effect was similar (see Figure 17); the most common path linked the variables unpleasant mother, hostile rejecting mother, negative identification with mother, childhood gender non-conformity, adolescent homosexual involvement, and adult homosexuality. Again, say Bell et al., childhood gender non-conformity was the second strongest predictor overall (53 percent), though it was less likely to develop among girls who reported "much identification with Mother," and was particularly strong for homosexual women (48 percent) who had masculine pastimes in childhood.

These Results were Significant

However, when Bell et al. summarize their results, they say none of the variables link into significant paths. Altogether they give their paths a value of something between 30 and 40 percent, and then dismiss this level as insignificant. But elsewhere in their study, they remark that 30 to 40 percent is commonly considered significant, and, indeed, it is by experts in path analysis. In the complicated real world, so many factors interact that even in a case in which the paths are obviously correct, only 30 to 40 percent of the causes may be picked up by this method. The conclusion seems to be, rather, that Bell et al. did find some significant paths, but seemed reluctant for some reason to say so. A fairer critical interpretation of their results is that the most common paths for male homosexuality and for lesbianism (described above) are among the most significant of the network of paths discovered.

Why weren't they more significant?

If you look at Figures 16 and 17, Childhood Gender Non-conformity, you will notice a vertical arrow: 0.88 in Figure 16, and 0.87 in Figure 17. Put a little simplistically, this is the amount of gender non-conformity that Bell et al. found their model was unable to explain. The figure actually translates to 77 percent. But the vertical arrow appears against most of the variables and the figures are high. For Homosexual Genital Activities in Childhood (Figure 16) 92 percent (0.96) of the causes were not explained by the study; 76 percent (0.87) of Childhood Gender Non-conformity (tomboyishness) in the female path analysis was unexplained; 58 percent (0.76) of female Adolescent Homosexual Involvement did not link with any of the preceding variables. This could mean either, or both, of two things.

The Right Questions and Unique Factors

One: the researchers did not ask the right questions. Two: individual and unique factors, which couldn't easily have been elicited by questions, contribute to the variables. If different questions had been asked, or if respondents had been able to offer their own opinions as to why they grew up homosexual, their responses could well have strengthened particular existing pathways, or unique experiences themselves might have emerged as one of the most significant pathways to homosexuality.

It is the nature of path analysis to eliminate those factors that do not apply to everyone in the sample in the simple attempt to find common factors. This is what Bell et al. did. But the net effect, as Van Wyk and Geist comment, is that "idiosyncratic and unique sexual and non-sexual experiences" as contributors to homosexuality are ruled out. Think of your own idiosyncratic and unique sexual and non-sexual experiences and judge whether or not you felt different as a result of those non-universal experiences.

For example, John mentions the day his father told him and his sister that he and his mother were divorcing, and he would have to live for the rest of his life with his mother. Lorna said she realized, as a child, that her mother could not be trusted, but that her father "had it good" while her mother had to work all the time. Roberta mentions an often-told story of the death of her father's

first wife in childbirth that filled her with fear of being
a woman. Then she was raped by her boyfriend. Steven
talks about his father favoring an older brother who was
good at sports while he wasn't. James mentions a rejection of his male genitalia at very young age, after he
observed violent sexual abuse of his mother by his father. Jane recalls frequent sexual contact with her father
who was not in other respects hostile to her. None of
these falls easily into the variables in Figures 16 and 17,
but all of these people identified these experiences as
critical in the development of their later homosexual
orientations.

Van Wyk and Geist

This path analysis was not looking for causes of homosexuality. It was an attempt to eliminate the bias in
Kinsey's sample to see how it affected homosexual incidence and distribution through the Kinsey classes. Kinsey
himself was not concerned to find causes of homosexuality, so his questions were not geared that way. So Van
Wyk and Geist's contribution from the Kinsey sample to
the debate on the development of homosexuality is inci-
dental rather than deliberate.

Nevertheless, what did they find? They found that
"intense sexual experiences and feelings of arousal and
pleasure or discomfort associated with those experiences
[were] the strongest precursors of sexual orientation."
All variables considered, they found higher levels of homosexuality among males in the Kinsey sample who reported "poorer teenage relationships with their fathers,
had more girl companions at age 10, fewer male companions at ages 10 and 16, avoided sports participation,
learned of homosexuality by experience, learned to
masturbate by being masturbated by a male, had intense
pre-pubertal sexual contact with boys or men, had neither heterosexual contact nor petting to orgasm by age
18, found thought or sight of males, (but not females)
arousing by age 18, had homosexual contact by age

18. . . . and had higher first year homosexual behavior activity."

For women they found more homosexuality among those who "had few girl companions at age 10 and few male companions at 16, had learned to masturbate by being masturbated by a female, had intense pre-pubertal sexual contact with boys or men, found thought or sight of females, but not males, arousing by age 18, had homosexual contact by age 18, and higher first-year homosexual behavior frequency."

All these variables together accounted for 36 percent of female homosexuality and 78 percent of male homosexuality. But, again, many individual variables were mostly unaccounted for.

Evidence of Environmental Conditioning

Bell et al. explained that the causality effect their model showed was misleading because some of the paths could be explained as the simple continuance of homosexual feelings and activities from adolescence into adulthood (Figure 16). Van Wyk and Geist made a similar comment about their own path analysis: "Once arousal to a particular type of stimulus occurs, it tends quite rapidly to form a pattern." In other words, we are talking less about causality in some cases than about the formation of a habit pattern in adolescence that simply continues on into adulthood. We are also talking about addictive patterns. (Continuing high levels of unsafe sex in the face of AIDS, by about one fifth of homosexual men, in spite of good understanding of transmission routes and risks, is good evidence that the behavior has become addictive.[4]) Habits and addictions have a high environmental component.

Summary

These two path analyses have been used to argue that there is no social or familial basis to homosexuality. That conclusion is not justified. For reasons that are not entirely clear, Bell et al. chose to say, even when their paths accounted for 30 percent to 40 percent of adult homosexuality, that the paths were not significant, even though it is well-established in path analysis that such a level of correlation is significant. They identified paths that lend support to psychological theories of homosexual development: negative relationships with same-sex parent, leading to lack of gender identification; gender non-conformity (sissiness in boys and tomboyism in girls); homosexual arousal in childhood and homosexual experience in adolescence in the search to re-connect to those of the same gender. These explanations are gaining increasing credibility among those who work with those homosexuals who want to change their orientation.

Van Wyk and Geist, although their raw material was not structured for a study of causality, nevertheless found environmental variables that accounted for 36 percent of female homosexuality and 78 percent of male homosexuality.

However, neither of the studies accounts very well for homosexuality in adults. Individual variables are mostly left unaccounted for, and what can appear to be a causal path from adolescence through to adulthood is sometimes really only the development and strengthening of a habit.

The two path analyses lend good support to the idea of a constellation of environmental factors behind homosexuality, rather than biological ones, with hints that existing paths might be strengthened if the right questions were asked, and respondents were able to volunteer reasons why they believed they became homosexual.

Notes

1. Bell, A.P., Weinberg, M.S., Hammersmith, S.K., *Sexual Preference: Its Development In Men and Women*

(Bloomington, IN: Indiana University Press, 1981).

2. Van Wyk, P.H., Geist, C.S., "Psychosocial development of heterosexual, bisexual and homosexual behavior," *Archives of Sexual Behavior* (1984): 13:505-544.

3. Whitam, F.L., Mathy, R.M., *Male Homosexuality in Four Societies, Brazil, Guatemala, the Philippines, and the United States* (New York: Praeger, 1986).

4. Dawson, J., Fitzpatrick, R., McLean, J., Hart, G., Boulton, M., "The HIV test and sexual behavior in a sample of homosexually active men," *Social Science and Medicine* (1991): 32:683-688.

Chapter Twelve

Can You Change
Your Sexual Orientation?

One of the strongest arguments against homosexuality as an inborn, unalterable condition is change in sexual orientation. The scientific literature shows that sexual orientation is anything but fixed and unalterable; rather, it shows that sexuality is fluid. People move around on the homosexual-heterosexual continuum to a surprising degree in both directions, but a far greater proportion of homosexuals become heterosexual than heterosexuals become homosexual. Some of the change is therapeutically assisted, but in some cases it appears to be almost random—circumstantial. Life itself can bring along the factor that makes the difference. This chapter looks at change and its proponents and opponents.

Spontaneous Change
Homosexual to Heterosexual

Bob is a former gay man whose father was sick most of his childhood and early teenage life. He grew up feeling homosexual attraction toward other men and had a lover for two years as a teenager. Two years after that relationship, he suddenly realized he wasn't struggling anymore with homosexual feelings. "As I look back now I see that part of the reason was that I was working with my father and having regular time with him for the first time in my life. I didn't realize what was going on, but a need was being met in my life, that I didn't know was there. I didn't struggle with homosexuality at that point."

Bob believes that his homosexuality was a search for
male affection and connection that had its roots in the
lack of a childhood relationship with his father. He was
much closer to his mother. When he began in his late
teens to work and relate with his father for the first time,
he believes he gained something from the relationship
that led to a diminution of his homosexual feelings.

One homosexual man found that when he joined the
Air Force, he began to notice women. The man was a
self-identified homosexual—not seeking to change his
orientation. "Being in a totally masculine environment I
started to relate to men more spontaneously and feel
better about my own masculinity. I felt I bridged a gap
between me and the straight males . . . like being one of
the guys and trusting each other. And as a result, all
sorts of blocks broke down. I seemed to start to notice
women . . . for the first time in my life I started having
sex dreams with women in them. I was still mostly turned
on by men, but suddenly, women too. It surprised the
hell out of me."[1]

Being able to trust straight males and become "one
of the guys" seemed to bridge a gap between himself
and heterosexual men that took him some distance along
the continuum toward heterosexuality. He became, in
effect, bisexual. The change led the authors of the paper
to remark on "the malleability and temporal
unpredictability of sexuality and sexual identity."

The work of Kinsey on male and female sexuality in
the forties and fifties is probably classic in the field in its
conclusions that sexual orientation is fluid and subject to
spontaneous change. At an early stage in his research
Kinsey (as cited by Pomeroy[2]) discovered "more than
eighty cases of [previously homosexual] men who had
made a satisfactory heterosexual adjustment." This was
2% of his sample. Small amounts of homosexual fantasy
remained; these men only just failed to make his Category
Zero—exclusive heterosexuality.

Commenting particularly on the work of Kinsey et al., Ross says, "Given these data . . . sexuality can thus be seen as a fluctuating variable rather than as a constant."[3]

A survey by the well known research team Bell, Weinberg and Hammersmith[4] published in 1981 also claimed that 2 percent of the heterosexual population said they had once been exclusively homosexual. Independently, Cameron et al.,[5] in 1985, reported an identical figure. Both these studies also put the incidence of homosexuality at 4 percent. In other words nearly half the homosexual sample moved significantly towards heterosexuality. But change was occurring in both directions. About 2 percent of the heterosexual group became homosexual (Figure 18). More data are available from the comprehensive study by Laumann et al. (1994),[6] who reported that about half those males homosexually active as young adults were no longer active later. Granted, only one or two incidences of activity were recorded, and questions were directed at activity rather than identity, but, as far as it goes, the survey supports the other studies. Hart[7] reported that roughly 1 percent of a group of conservative Christian men spontaneously reported in a questionnaire they had once been exclusively homosexual but now were happy and adjusted heterosexuals.

Homosexuality is more fluid than heterosexuality as shown by the large proportion of homosexuals who move toward a heterosexual orientation, compared with the small proportion of heterosexuals who become homosexual. Homosexuality is about twenty-five times more subject to change.

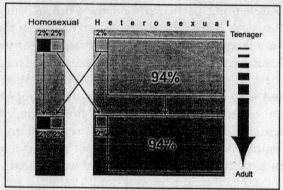

At least three surveys suggest that about half of all males who classify themselves "homosexual" earlier in life (probably as teenagers) classify themselves "heterosexual" as adults.[1] But only 2% of people classing themselves as heterosexual early in life become homosexual in adulthood. So change in sexual orientation certainly occurs - mainly towards heterosexuality.

Figure 18:

The sexology literature reports a huge number of examples of change of all degrees from homosexuality to or toward heterosexuality. These studies have been so numerous that West takes an entire chapter in his classic book, *Homosexuality Re-examined,* to review them, and comments: "Although some militant homosexuals find such claims improbable and unpalatable, authenticated accounts have been published of apparently exclusive and long-standing homosexuals unexpectedly changing their orientation."[8]

West mentions one man who was exclusively homosexual for eight years, then became heterosexual. *Straight,* a book written by a man with the pseudonym Aaron, in 1972, describes Aaron's thorough immersion in the gay scene, his decision to leave it, and his arousal of feelings for women and subsequent marriage.[9]

Ross[3] surveyed homosexuals married to heterosexuals. Seventy percent said their homosexuality never really varied in intensity throughout their marriage, but 25 percent said it became more intense* and 5 percent said it became less intense. A 5 percent figure for spontaneous decrease in homosexual preference is small, but it seems even these changes were real.

Nichols[10] says some life-long female homosexuals spontaneously develop heterosexual interests and become bisexual in mid-life. She even thinks there is evidence (uncited) that this may be getting more frequent.

Another well known author in the field, Hatterer, who believes in sexual orientation change, said, "I've heard of hundreds of . . . men who went from a homosexual to a heterosexual adjustment on their own."[11]

Among the Sambia, a Papua-New Guinean tribe in which homosexual sex was culturally prescribed for growing boys until marriageable age (when they were expected to be exclusively heterosexual), there was a significant change toward heterosexuality. Herdt,[12] who has intensively researched the Sambia, graded individual males on the Kinsey scale for those two periods: before and after marriage. He found that the change from adolescent to married man in attitudes and behavior equated to a move from Kinsey homosexual classes five and six to Class two, predominantly heterosexual.† Herdt believed the change was a real change in sexual orientation.

Heterosexual to Homosexual

Exclusively heterosexual women can, in mid-life, develop lesbian feelings and behavior. This is a well known clinical feature of lesbianism.[8] It often occurs during marriage or after marriage break-up, with no clinically

---

*This group may have comprised most of about one third of adult homosexuals who only become fully aware of themselves as homosexual after they marry.[3, 46]

†Kinsey's method of grading sexual orientation according to an individual's most homosexual three years over a period, regardless of present fantasy and behavior, may have under-estimated the movement towards heterosexuality in the Sambia.

observable hint of prior existence—not even lesbian fantasy.

Nichols[10] found among married bisexual women that "many appeared to make dramatic swings in Kinsey ratings of both behavior and fantasy over the course of the marriage" in ways that "cast doubt upon the widely held belief in the inflexibility of sexual orientation and attraction over a lifetime."

Dixon[13] surveyed fifty women who became bisexual after the age of thirty. They were exclusively heterosexual before, having had no earlier significant sexual fantasy about females, and quite heterosexually satisfied. They continued to enjoy promiscuous sexual relationships with both sexes.

Assisted Change

If considerable swings in sexual orientation can happen without therapeutic intervention, it makes sense they would be even more considerable if they are therapeutically encouraged in a motivated person.

The first recorded instance of assisted change may be in the New Testament. In I Corinthians 6:9ff, Paul, writing to the Corinthians, said about homosexuals (the word translated homosexuals is *arsenokoitai* in the Greek, meaning "male/coitus"): ". . . that is what some of you were. But you were washed, you were sanctified, you were justified in the name of the Lord Jesus Christ and by the Spirit of our God." They changed, and it is reasonable to believe—given the emphasis in Christianity on inward attitude rather than merely outward behaviors—that the change was not merely behavioral.

Assisted change has been attempted since last century, using many techniques, including hypnosis, aversion therapy, behavioral therapy, psychoanalysis; some rather brutal, some a lot more successful than others. At an early stage in his research Kinsey "recommended a pattern of treatment to those who wished to change"[2] In prescribing this course to those who wanted to take it,

Kinsey always warned that "he had known it to be successful in many cases, but he had also seen it fail."

But it seems whatever the therapy used there was always some change toward heterosexuality. Dr. Reuben Fine, Director of the New York Centre for Psychoanalytic Training, remarked: "If patients are motivated to change, a considerable percentage of overt homosexuals (become) heterosexuals."[14] Dr. Bernard Berkowitz and Mildred Newman: "We've found that a homosexual who really wants to change has a very good chance of doing so."[15] Dr. Edmund Bergler concludes after analysis and consultations with 600 homosexuals over thirty years: "Homosexuality has an excellent prognosis in psychiatric-psychoanalytic treatment of one to two years duration . . . provided the patient really wishes to change. Cure denotes not bi-sexuality, but real and unfaked heterosexuality."[16] After twenty years of comparative study of homosexuals and heterosexuals, Dr. Irving Bieber wrote: "Reversal [homosexual to heterosexual] estimates now range from 30 percent to an optimistic 50 percent."[17] Bieber followed some of his psychoanalytical clients for as long as ten years and found they had remained exclusively heterosexual.[18]

Dr. Charles Socarides said: "There is . . . sufficient evidence that in a majority of cases homosexuality can be successfully treated by psychoanalysis."[19] Scientists Masters and Johnson, after work with sixty-seven homosexuals and fourteen lesbians who requested reversion therapy, reported a success rate of 71.6 percent after a follow-up of six years. Although they have been criticized for serious flaws in their post-therapy follow-up and assessment, it seems certain they produced many real and lasting reversions.[20]

Psychologist Dr. Gerard van den Aardweg, after twenty years research into treatment of homosexuality, stated: "Two thirds reached a stage where homosexual feelings were occasional impulses at most, or completely absent."[21] Psychiatrist Dr. William Wilson claimed a 55 percent success rate in treating homosexuals who were professing Christians.[22] According to Dr. Robert Kronemeyer, a clinical psychologist: "About 80 percent of homosexual men and women in syntonic therapy have been able to free themselves, and achieve a healthy and satisfying heterosexual adjustment."[23]

One of the well-documented changes[24] happened by accident. Two Florida medical professionals reported in 1993 that they treated a homosexual man for social phobia—he had extreme anxiety in any social setting. He had been exclusively homosexual in fantasy and practice since adolescence, but this was unconnected with his request for treatment; he was quite happy as a homosexual. The drug Phenelzine helps many cases of social phobia and certainly did in his case. By the fourth week, he had become more outgoing, talkative, and comfortable in social situations. He spoke spontaneously in groups without blushing. But, curiously, he reported a positive, pleasurable experience of meeting and dating a woman. "During the next two months, he began dating females exclusively, reportedly enjoying heterosexual intercourse and having no sexual interest in males. He expressed a desire for a wife and family, and his sexual fantasies became entirely heterosexual. . . . In retrospect [he] decided that the combination of his anxiety when approaching and meeting people, the teasing rejection by heterosexual males, and the comfortable acceptance by homosexual males who pursued and courted him, had helped convince him of his homosexuality." So this report is of someone clearly exclusively homosexual whose behavior, in three months, became exclusively heterosexual.

One of the most significant recent surveys showing change was released by the California-based National Association for Research and Therapy of Homosexuality (NARTH) in May 1997.[25] It was conducted among nearly 860 homosexual individuals seeking a heterosexual identity, and more than 200 therapists and psychologists treating them, and showed a large shift in sexual orientation toward heterosexuality after therapy. Before treatment, 68 percent of respondents viewed themselves as exclusively or almost entirely homosexual, and another 22 percent as more homosexual than heterosexual. After treatment, only 13 percent still felt they were still exclusively or entirely homosexual, but 33 percent described themselves as either exclusively or almost entirely heterosexual.

Ex-gay support groups say hundreds of homosexuals have moved significantly toward a heterosexual orientation as a result of Christian commitment and the specialized support and services of ex-gay groups.

West, summarizing the mainstream material,[8] says that behavioral techniques appeared to have the best rate of success (never less than 30 percent). Although psychoanalysis claimed a great deal of success, the average rate seemed to be about 25 percent. (But 50 percent of bisexuals achieved exclusive heterosexuality.)

One developmental research psychologist, Dr. Elizabeth Moberly, argues that the success rate of psychotherapy in homosexual reparative therapy has not been higher because of inadequate understanding of the causes of homosexuality. Rates of success obviously reflect the relevance of the treatment model. Moberly maintains that, until the eighties, psychotherapy was still viewing homosexuality as an opposite-sex problem rather than a difficulty in relating with the same sex. In her opinion, this explains the disillusionment of many homosexuals who unsuccessfully sought therapy in the past. It may be that the increasingly widespread adoption of Moberly's treatment model in the last fifteen years is reflected in the higher than average recovery figures demonstrated by NARTH.

However, even where it is inadequately informed, psychotherapy produces change wherever it impinges on issues relevant to the causes of homosexuality. As West comments in his review of the literature, "Every study ever performed on conversion from homosexual

to heterosexual orientation has produced some successes."[8] Dr. Reuben Fine similarly remarks, "all studies
from Schrenk-Notzing [last century] on have found positive effects virtually regardless of the kind of treatment
used."[14] According to West, those most likely to respond
to treatment are clients with a good level of motivation,
a history of some heterosexual feelings, and who have
entered the gay lifestyle later.

But, in 1973, the American Psychiatric Association
(APA) removed homosexuality as a disorder from its
Diagnostic and Statistical Manual of Psychiatric Disorders
(DSM-II), and redefined it as a condition only to be
treated if the client was distressed—in which case he or
she should be counselled to come to terms with the orientation. More recently, the APA Board recommended a
resolution banning homosexual reparative therapy. The
move failed only because of aggressive lobbying by the
resolution's opponents.[26]

In view of the evidence that change is possible, what
was going on?

The Official Attitude of the Professions

The APA's decision to declassify homosexuality as a
disorder has been acknowledged by gay activists as one
of their victories. The details are well documented, and
the role of gay activists in the process is not really dis-
puted. The APA, after months of harassment and intimi-
dation by activists (who disrupted scientific research and
conferences, forged credentials, and physically intimi-
dated psychiatrists) made a "medical judgment" to re-
move homosexuality from the diagnostic manual by a
vote of only 34 percent of its members. Although a survey conducted by the journal *Medical Aspects of Human
Sexuality* four years later showed 69 percent of the 2500
psychiatrists who responded opposed the 1973 action,[27]
the effect of the decision was to inhibit scientific research, influence student training programs, and, in an

age of minority rights, make reparative therapy politically incorrect. According to Nicolosi, one of the founders of NARTH, the decision effectively silenced professional discussion of homosexuality as a disorder.[25] Many mental health professionals are now simply ignorant or disbelieving of change, untutored in how to bring it about, lack the personal courage to stand against the tide, or are ideologically committed to the gay agenda. The pressure on the APA to put an end to reparative therapy has continued. One of the most powerful voices inside the APA in this regard is that of Dr. Richard Isay, an openly gay man, and chairman of the APA committee on Gay, Lesbian and Bisexual issues, who is emphatically against homosexual conversion therapy, which he has called "the greatest abuse of psychiatry in America today." Isay remains convinced that "most, though not all, dynamically oriented psychiatrists in general and psychologists in particular [believe] that homosexuality can and should be changed to heterosexuality," a state of affairs he is committed to changing.[28] In the meantime, the Washington State Psychological Association issued an advisory policy strongly opposing any form of sexual-orientation conversion therapy, and gay activists targeted Nicolosi's publisher with dozens of angry phone calls and about 100 letters after the publication of a book discussing reparative therapy for male homosexuals.[29]

The National Association for Psychoanalytic Research and Therapy of Homosexuals (NARTH) was founded in 1992 by those psychiatrists who believe the condition treatable and who seek to counteract the effect of pro-gay propaganda on official policy and on individual psychologists and psychiatrists. After one year, about fifty professionals had joined, and by October 1998, membership had swelled to over 800.

The Formation of "Ex-gay" Groups

An interesting development followed the APA's deci-

sion in 1973 and a companion move by the American
Psychological Association. Looking for therapeutic help
that was no longer available, men in the process of changing their orientation began to set up support groups to
help each other. Late in the seventies, they began to join
forces and to proliferate. There are now at least 150 of
these groups in the USA, Europe, South East Asia, and
Australia. They have come to be known as "ex-gay"
groups—the largest being a confederation of groups called
Exodus International.

There is an interesting parallel between the rise of
ex-gay groups and that of Alcoholics Anonymous (AA).
AA came on the scene at a time when the medical profession thought alcoholism was incurable, or at least didn't
know how to help. Bill Wilson, a recovered alcoholic and
founder of AA, was invited to speak on 24 May 1949 at
an alcoholism symposium presented by the APA in
Montreal. As the record reads, a past president of the
APA said, "outside of the few AAs in the room, and
myself, I do not think a single one of my colleagues
believed a word of your explanation." When Bill Wilson
expressed surprise because of the applause he had received, the man replied, "Well, Mr. Wilson, you AAs
have a hundred thousand recoveries, and we in the psychiatric profession have only a few. They were applaud-
ing the results much more than the message."[30]

Alcoholics Anonymous came on the scene when the
medical profession had no answers for the alcoholic; ex-
gay groups surfaced at a time when the APA backed away
from reparative therapy for homosexuals.

AA had its detractors: people said the stories sounded
spurious or they didn't like the "God rackets" (AA's
Twelve Steps require a relationship with God—as He is
understood). Bill Wilson's right hand man relapsed, some
members got drunk again, one at least committed suicide. The ex-gay movement has its detractors too, and
for similar reasons. Gay activists in particular like to

quote the relapse of an ex-gay leader, Michael Bussee, in the ex-gay movement's early history. AA today has wide credibility and an unofficial success rate of something like 25 percent, and it is quite possible that in several decades the general public will be as aware that gays can change their orientation as they are now aware that alcoholics can achieve permanent sobriety—the difference being that the reformed alcoholic cannot take another drink, but the ex-gay movement believes the former homosexual can form non-erotic relationships with other males.

It appears that those who insist on 100 percent success rates in any field of therapy as proof of its effectiveness will never find them. AA believes that those who "work the program" will find their way out, and that many, for their own reasons, simply do not work the program. Success rates of about 25 percent are not uncommon in many programs offering recovery from problem behaviors with a strongly addictive component. Behaviors often become addictive when they are used to relieve unresolved emotional pain. Those in therapy often find it easier to continue the addiction than to refuse it and begin to deal with underlying motivations. Homosexuality appears to be little different. According to psychiatrist Cappon, psychologists can be confident that change occurs "at least as frequently in homosexual persons as in people afflicted by any other personality disorder."[31]

Why does the gay activist resist change?

Gay activism usually comes up with any or all of the following arguments.

• The individuals concerned were never homosexual in the first place.

• The alleged change in orientation that has taken place is brief and illusory. (Given time the person will revert; the change is only the result of suppression of homosexual feelings which will resurface.)

• A person can change his or her identity but not the orientation. (You can stop acting homosexually, but you can't stop being inwardly homosexual.)

• Those who say change is possible are "homophobic" (hating or fearful of homosexuality and homosexuals). That is, they are forcing homosexuals to become heterosexual because they don't like homosexuality or homosexuals.

• Homosexuals who undergo this change are emotionally damaged in the process, become depressed, lose self-esteem, and become suicidal because they are doing violence to their true selves and "internalizing" the "homophobia" that is forcing change on them.

We estimate gay activists comprise 1 to 10 percent of all sexually active homosexuals. In an age dedicated to democratic rights and freedoms, they have succeeded in defining themselves as a minority group unjustly suffering discrimination and are seeking equality with heterosexuals in all possible respects. Gay activism attempts to discredit any research that shows change is possible or anyone who claims to have changed. Why?

People who are now gay lived for a long time with the growing awareness of their homosexual orientation, hyper-conscious of majority attitudes towards homosexuality, fearful of disclosure, not knowing what to do about it. Many tried alone for years to change but failed. Some genuinely sought help from counselors, ministers of religion, psychologists, or psychiatrists—often at considerable expense—but got nowhere. It's not too surprising that many believe it's impossible to change. "If it were possible, I would be heterosexual today," some of them say. If they turned to religion, as many of them did, and found only censure, rejection, and no power to change, they will be cynical about the church unless it accepts them unconditionally. Nearly 40 percent of gays say that, because of their homosexuality, they have become less religious than they were.[32] Gays who find no way to change their orientation have few options, but one of them is to summon the considerable personal courage required to accept the label "homosexual" and "come out" to themselves, families, and others. But a decision in which there is such an enormous personal investment then has to be justified, sustained, and validated, and gay activism works hard to this end on many fronts. Naturally, when governments begin granting political protections, and homosexuality begins getting official ecclesiastical endorsement, support from medical and caring professions, "scientific" backing, and media affirmation, change is not something a self-identified gay person needs to give much thought to—especially if there are rewarding patterns of sexual gratification to give up. As one ex-gay, Frank Worthen, put it, after almost thirty years out of homosexuality, "Sex has met their needs for closeness for so long that the prospect of giving it up is very threatening." He goes on to say, "There is no-one in the lifestyle who cannot make the change—but many will be too fearful to seek it."[33]

It becomes easier to argue that heterosexual intolerance and discrimination are the only reasons homosexuals want to change their orientation than to believe change is possible. Ross, for example, argues no homosexual's request for help to change is voluntary.[3]

But in spite of this, about half of lesbians and about 62 percent of gay men want to change their orientation at some time in their lives.[34] According to Bell and Weinberg[32] in 1978, about one in four lesbians and one in five males actually tried to do something about it, and almost half of them made two or more attempts. That was the situation in the seventies, though increased public acceptance of homosexuality has probably reduced those figures.

But, perhaps because the ex-gay movement is becoming increasingly visible, more and more people are seeking help to change. They come for the following reasons.

Short-lived and Unstable Relationships

A good number of homosexuals find after a time that, in spite of the excitement, homosexuality does not yield the promised satisfaction. Mr. Right doesn't appear, or does, but sooner or later becomes Mr. Wrong.[35] Hooker[35] found that almost all homosexuals have "an intense longing for relationships with stability, continuity, intimacy, love and affection but are unable to find it." West comments that male relationships frequently break up "from internal dissension rather than outside pressure." Sixty percent of male relationships last less than a year, and most lesbian relationships less than three years. Affairs of five years or more are exceptional.[8] According to Pollak, male relationships rarely last longer than two years on average.[35a] The real life of the overt male gay is "replete with jealousy, competitiveness, insecurity, malice, tantrums and hysterical mood shifts" says West. Pollak says homosexual relationships are "often bedevilled from the start by dramas, anguish and infidelities," intense dependency, jealousy, and rage.[35a]

Unfaithfulness

Even in spite of "intense longings for stability and continuity," gay monogamous relationships are rarely faithful. "Monogamous" seems to imply some primary emotional commitment, while casual sex continues on the side.[42] McWhirter and Mattison,[43] a gay couple who are psychiatrist and psychologist, attempted to disprove the notion that gay relationships did not last. In their book, *The Male Couple*, they report the results. They finally located 156 male couples who had been together between one and thirty-seven years, two thirds of whom had entered their relationships with expectations of faithfulness. Only seven had been able to maintain sexual fidelity, and, of those, none had been together more than five years. They could not find one couple who had been faithful beyond five years.

Compulsive Behavior

Terms like "compulsive," "hyper-sexual," and "addictive" are turning up more and more in studies of gay sexuality. Quadland and Shattls, remark:

> For some a lack of choice is involved. . . . They reported not feeling in control of their sexual behavior, reported having more sex than they wanted, and reported feeling victimized by their frequent sexual activity . . . the primary motivation and satisfaction appeared often not to be purely sexual. . . . A pattern of sexual control emerged which seemed most closely related to that of overeating.[37]

Pincu, comments that the main features of addictions are present in much gay sexual behavior, and the behavior is mood-altering.

> The excitement is not unlike that of a child discovering something new or forbidden, is a strong motivating force in the continued search for gratification and temporary self-esteem. . . . All the traditional defences of repression, rationalizing, minimizing, and intellectualizing are used by the compulsive individual to avoid admitting there is a problem and that his life is out of control.[38]

Homosexual promiscuity is well documented. In 1978 almost half of white homosexual males had had at least 500 different partners, and 28 percent had had 1000 or more, mostly strangers.[32] Homosexuals still have 3-4 times as many partners as heterosexuals,[6] and between 17 percent and 54 percent of gays continue to practice high-risk sex post-AIDS, suggesting an addictive drive. This is in spite of high levels of knowledge of HIV transmission routes, AIDS prevention counseling, positive HIV status, special safe-sex campaigns, and deaths of friends through AIDS.[39] It seems clear that a significant amount of homosexual behavior is out of control. Sexual behavior that is out of control does not increase anyone's self-respect; ultimately a cycle of using and being used leads to a sense of helplessness and depression.[40] Ex-gay groups say men seeking help often say they feel used. This is not to say that all homosexuals are promiscuous. Some are celibate, but they appear to constitute only a small minority of self-identified homosexuals. According to a long term study of homosexual men in England and Wales published in 1992, only 6 percent had had no sex in the last year.[41] West noted an "obsessive preoccupation with sexual topics whenever gay circles foregather" and "often a dislike of being tied down, leading to many partners."

Loneliness with Increasing Age

Male homosexuals become isolated with age. Gagnon and Simon comment, "serious feelings of depression or loneliness are often attendant on . . . the middle to late thirties."[36]

A future with no family life, children, or grandchildren can mean a bleak future for the non-married homosexual who becomes less attractive as he ages and does not feel accepted by the heterosexual community.

Conscience

But the gay lifestyle is not unrelieved misery. Some gays and lesbians don't leave it for any of the above reasons. They have plenty of good times and would be happy to stay where they are if it weren't for what they would probably call their conscience—a persistent sense that what they're doing is not what they're meant to be doing. They would be reluctant to describe this as "internalised homophobia."

Fear of Change

Ex-gays who have spent years in the gay scene say many gays would get out of the scene if only they knew how. Given the abundant statistical evidence of change, the attempt by gay activists to discredit the change process is a form of discrimination against a significant group of homosexuals who want to change. Dr. Fine remarks, "The misinformation . . . that homosexuality is untreatable by psychotherapy does incalculable harm to thousands of men and women."[14] Dr. Bergler insists, "The homosexual's real enemy is his ignorance of the possibility that he can be helped."[16] Masters and Johnson comment, "No longer should the qualified psychotherapist avoid the responsibility of either accepting the homosexual client in treatment or . . . referring him or her to an acceptable treatment source."[20] Dr. Tiffany Barnhouse, Professor of Psychiatry at Southern Methodist University states: "The frequent claim by 'gay' activists that it is impossible for homosexuals to change their orientation is categorically untrue. Such a claim accuses scores of conscientious, responsible psychiatrists and psychologists of falsifying their data."[44]

The Change Process

Ex-gay groups, and those therapists working with homosexuals seeking to change, identify several major issues needing attention: severe breaches in the relationship with the parent of the same-sex and refusal to role-model, unhappy same-sex peer group relationships, sexual abuse, eroticization of unmet needs for affection, confusion of sex with love, and an addictive cycle of sexual gratification. In females the addictive cycle is less sexual than emotional. The groups say the problem is deep-seated and to beat it takes dedication, patience, honest self-examination, and a lot of support. Ex-gays tend to say two things are essential: a complete break with the gay lifestyle (leaving the current relationship, and the gay milieu, moving out of the area if necessary), and a strong heterosexual support network to replace the gay support structure. Ex-gay groups belong to a family of support groups dealing with problem behaviors. Most of these make an appeal to a higher power. In ex-gay groups, the appeal is specifically to God, who is represented as loving and understanding—unlike many gay perceptions of God. They work to raise levels of self-esteem. Groups say that accountability, constant support, confrontation, help in dealing with the addictive cycle (identifying and avoiding triggers), and forming non-defensive, non-erotic friendships with people of the same sex lead to gradual but steady shifts in sexual orientation toward heterosexuality and the development of hetero-sexual attraction. Members are encouraged to forgive parents and reconcile. Lesbians in particular receive help for high levels (85 to 90 percent) of male sexual abuse.

Ex-gay groups are often unwilling to specify a time frame for the transition process, but change appears to be slow and steady. Some therapists and ex-gay groups say compulsive drives can fall to controllable levels in eighteen months to two years and steadily diminish there-after. It appears that after he or she is no longer acting out compulsively, the "ex-gay" is not too different from people seeking help for heterosexual problem behav-iors. Courses run by ex-gay groups often examine and help group members resolve "underlying" attitudes that they say prop up the homosexual condition, like resent-ment, unforgiveness, fear, anger, insecurity, rejection, envy, isolation, pride, anti-authority attitudes, defensive ways of relating, low self-esteem, manipulation, and the need to be in control. Ex-gay groups claim that those who have worked through the issues are genuinely no longer homosexual on the inside—not merely suppressed homosexuals who appear heterosexual on the outside. Many ex-gays go on to marry. (A fuller discussion of the change process may be found elsewhere.[33])

Gay activists have attacked the change process, say-ing it is injurious to self-esteem and can make gays sui-cidal and depressed. However, a survey by Mesmer found the opposite. Mesmer surveyed 100 people who had sought help toward a change of sexual orientation. He found that 88 percent felt "more able to have friendly relationships" and felt "more self-respect." Ninety-seven percent of men felt more masculine, and 77 percent of women more feminine. Seventeen of the respondents had married, 55 percent reported "exclusively heterosexual interest," and 47 percent some homosexual interest that they "rarely felt compelled to act out." Thirteen per cent still had some homosexual behavior. Ninety four percent felt closer to God.[45] The NARTH survey also found an improvement in psychological well-being and inter-personal relationships as a result of reparative therapy.

Ex-gay groups argue that homosexuality itself is a symptom of poor self-esteem, saying that a boy or girl who has not bonded with a same-sex parent, has felt different from and excluded by peers, and has often been sexually abused, will not have high levels of self-esteem. Sexual behavior which is out of control also leads to depression. Homosexuals and lesbians attempt suicide roughly three times more often than heterosexuals[32]—a statistic that has often been blamed on societal attitudes. But, according to Bell and Weinberg, gay suicide attempts, when they are directly related to homosexuality, are often over the break-up of a relationship.[32]

It seems quite unfair, therefore, to claim, as gay activism does, that those who try to help motivated homosexuals change are homophobic. To be consistent, they would have to argue that Alcoholics Anonymous hates alcoholics.

Although gay activists say that those who claim to have changed were obviously never homosexual in the first place, hundreds of homosexuals making the transition can talk of years of homosexual desire and attraction, homosexual activity, or of lovers, live-in relationships, promiscuity and political activism. One former gay man, the Rev. David Kyle Foster, often answers those who doubt he was ever really homosexual in the first place, "Would making love to over 1000 men count?"

Although gays want proof that no homosexual thought will ever occur again, ex-gay groups say such a demand is unrealistic. They report that homosexual urges gradually become controllable and continue to diminish steadily, while heterosexual interest begins to develop. Many ex-gays marry happily. In the words of one veteran ex-gay, Alan Medinger, "some little thing might zing 'em periodically. But it's really nothing more than a nuisance." Ex-gays in treatment are taught to identify what they are really seeking when a homosexual impulse occurs, and to set about getting it non-erotically. In males, it is often a need to be affirmed as a male by another male.

Summary

There is abundant documentation that homosexuals can move toward a heterosexual orientation, often with therapeutic assistance, sometimes without it. Obviously, sexual orientation is fluid, not fixed, so that it is impossible to argue it is genetically pre-determined.

Notes

1. Blumstein, P.W., Schwartz, P., "Bisexuality in men," *Urban Life* (1976): 5:339-358.

2. Pomeroy, W.B., *Dr. Kinsey and the Institute for Sex Research* (New York: Harper and Row, 1972).

3. Ross, M.W., *The Married Homosexual Man* (London: Routledge & Kegan Paul, 1993).

4. Bell, A.P., Weinberg, M.S., Hammersmith, S.K., *Sexual Preference: Its Development In Men and Women* (Bloomington, IN: Indiana University Press, 1981).

5. Cameron, P., Proctor, K., Coburn, K., Forde, N., "Sexual orientation and sexually transmitted disease," *Nebraska Medical Journal* (1985): 70:292-299.

6. Laumann, E.O., Gagnon, J.H., Michael, R.T., Michaels, S., *The Social Organization of Sexuality* (Chicago: Univer-

sity of Chicago Press, 1994).

7. Hart, A.D., *The Sexual Man* (Dallas, TX: Word, 1994).

8. West, D.J., *Homosexuality Reexamined* (Duckworth, London: 1977).

9. Aaron, W., *Straight* (New York: Bantam Books, 1972).

10. Nichols, M., "Bisexuality in women. Myths, realities and implications for therapy," *Women and Therapy* (1988): 7:235-252.

11. Hatterer, L.J., *Changing Homosexuality in the Male* (New York: McGraw-Hill, 1970).

12. Herdt, G.H., "Guardians of the Flutes," *Idioms of Masculinity* (New York: McGraw-Hill, 1981).

13. Dixon, J.K., "Sexuality and relationship changes in married females following the commencement of bisexual activity," *Journal of Homosexuality* (1985): 11:115-133.

14. Fine, R., *Psychoanalytic Theory, Male and Female Homosexuality Psychological Approaches* (Washington: Hemisphere Publishing Corporation, 1987).

15. Newman, M., Berkowitz, B., Owen, J., *How to Be Your Own Best Friend* (New York: Lark Publishing Company, 1971).

16. Bergler, E., *Homosexuality: Disease or Way of Life* (New York: Collier Books, 1962).

17. Bieber, I., *Homosexuality: A Psychoanalytic Study* (New York: Basic Books, 1962).

18. Bieber, I., Bieber, T.B., "Male Homosexuality," *Canadian Journal of Psychiatry* (1979): 24:416.

19. Socarides, C.W., *Homosexuality* (New York: Jason Aronson, 1978).

20. Masters, W.H., Johnson, V.E., *Homosexuality In Perspective* (Boston: Little, Brown and Company, 1979).

21. van den Aardweg, G., *Homosexuality and Hope: A Psychologist Talks about Treatment and Change* (Ann Arbor, MI: Servant Books, Ann Arbor, 1986).

22. Anon., "Gays can change says psychiatrist," *Exodus Standard* (February 1989): 66.

23. Kronemeyer, R., *Overcoming Homosexuality* (New York: Macmillan, 1980).

24. Golwyn, D.H., Sevlie, C.P., "Adventitious change in homosexual behavior during treatment of social phobia with phenelzine," *Journal of Clinical Psychiatry* (1993): 54:39-40.

25. NARTH, *New Study Confirms Homosexuality Can Be Overcome* (Encino, CA: NARTH, 1997).

26. Socarides, C.W., *Homosexuality: A Freedom Too Far* (Phoenix, AR: Adam Margrave Books, 1995).

27. Prager, D., "Judaism, Homosexuality and Civilization," *Ultimate Issues* (1990): 6:24.

28. Isay, R., "Letter to the editor," *New York Times* (25 April 1993): E16.

29. Anon., "Psychoanalysts say change is possible," *Exodus Standard* (February 1992): 94.

30. Alcoholics Anonymous World Service, *Pass It On* (New York: Alcoholics Anonymous World Service, 1984).

31. Cappon, D.J., *Toward an Understanding of Homosexuality* (Englewood Cliffs, NJ: Prentice-Hall, 1965).

32. Bell, A.P., Weinberg, M.S., *Homosexualities: A Study of Diversity Among Men and Women* (New York: Simon and Schuster, 1978).

33. Whitehead, B.K., *Craving for Love* (Tunbridge Wells, United Kingdom: Monarch, 1993).

34. Saghir, M.T., Robins, E., *Male and Female Homosexuality, A Comprehensive Investigation* (Baltimore, MD: Wil-

liams and Wilkins, 1973).

35. Nicolosi, J., *Reparative Therapy of Male Homosexuality* (Northvale, NJ: Jason Aronson, Inc., 1991).

35a. Pollak, M., "Male homosexuality—or happiness in the ghetto," In *Western Sexuality* edited by P. Ariès and A. Béjin (Oxford: Basil Blackwell, 1985), 40-61.

36. Gagnon, J.H., Simon, W., *Sexual Conduct* (London: Hutchinson, 1974).

37. Quadland, M.C., Shattls, W.D., "AIDS, sexuality and sexual control," *Journal of Homosexuality* (1987): 14:277-298.

38. Pincu, L., "Sexual compulsivity in gay men: controversy and treatment," *Journal of Counselling and Development* (1989): 68:63-66.

39. Whitehead, N.E., Whitehead, B.K., *Submission to the Justice and Law Reform Select Committee on the Human Rights Commission Amendment Bill 1992* (Lower Hutt, New Zealand: Lion of Judah Ministries, 1993).

40. Seligman, M.E.P., *Helplessness—On Depression, Development and Death* (London: Freeman, 1975).

41. Brown, P., "Dangers of monogamy," *New Scientist,* (21 November 1992): 135:38-39.

42. Connell, R.W., Crawford, J., Dowsett, G.W., Kippax, S., Sinnott, V., Rodden, P., Berg, R., Baxter, D., Watson, L., "Danger and context: unsafe anal sexual practice among homosexual and bisexual men in the AIDS crisis," *Australian and New Zealand Journal of Sociology* (1990): 26:187-208.

43. McWhirter, D.P., Mattison, A.M., *The Male Couple* (Englewood Cliffs, NJ: Prentice-Hall, Englewood Cliffs, 1984).

44. Barnhouse, R.T., "What is a Christian view of homosexuality?" *Circuit Rider* (12 February 1984).

45. Mesmer, R., "Homosexuals who change lifestyles," *The Journal of Christian Healing* (1992): 14:12-17.

46. Wolf, T.J., "Marriages of bisexual men," *Journal of Homosexuality* (1985): 11:135-148.

Minimal Genetic Contribution to Homosexuality

Those researchers who know most about genes say, "Your genes did not make you do it." Let's review the evidence, particularly as it relates to homosexuality, bearing in mind that these arguments hold for all human behaviors to a greater or lesser extent.

• Science has not yet discovered any genetically dictated behavior in humans. So far, genetically dictated behaviors of the one-gene-one-trait variety have been found only in very simple organisms. The closest thing to a genetically-caused human behavior that science has come up with in humans so far (aggression in Dutch men related to a mutation of one gene), is far too responsive to counseling and too varied in its expression to be genetically determined. This raises the obvious question: is there really any such thing as a genetically-caused human behavior?

• If we want to argue that human behavior is genetically caused, most geneticists would say many genes would have to be involved. Even the most liberal behavioral scientist would argue for the involvement of at least five or six genes in a particular behavior; others would argue for hundreds. But if many genes are involved in a behavior, then changes in that behavior will tend to take place very slowly and steadily (say, changes of a few percent each generation over many generations, perhaps thirty). That being so, homosexuality could not appear and disappear suddenly in family trees the way it does. For it to do so, many "homosexual" recessive genes would have to switch on suddenly in the fetus, and all the "heterosexual" genes would have to switch off—a nearly impossible scenario from a geneticist's point of view. About as easy as breeding petrifying fear into rats in a single generation.

• The human race shares most of its genes—something between 99.7 percent and 99.9 percent of them, according to one estimate. That means all ethnic groups will have most of them. This has three implications.

1. If homosexuality is genetically dictated, homosexual practices will be identical or very similar in all cultures. But the range and diversity of homosexual practice and customs among different cultures, and even within cultures, argues against any genetically-mandated homosexuality.

2. So many genes held in common by all ethnic groups would argue for a similar incidence of homosexuality in all cultures. But homosexuality has been unknown in some cultures and mandatory in others.

3. Just as changes in behavior will take place very slowly in a family tree—over very many generations— where there are many genes involved, so changes in practice and behavior will take place very slowly, over many centuries in cultures. So the decline of whole models of homosexuality (the Greek, over a couple of centuries, and the Melanesian, within a century); the relatively sudden (in genetic terms) emergence of the present Western model over a couple of centuries; and abrupt changes of practice within an ethnic group, even over a single generation, are not consistent with anything genetic. Even less so the swiftly changing sexual practices within the current Western model.

• If homosexuality were genetically dictated or strongly influenced, there is no way a "homosexual gene" or "genes" could maintain themselves in the population.

One adult needs to have an average of one child if a specific gene, or many specific genes, present in the adult are to stay in the gene pool. But, on average, five "exclusive" homosexuals produce only one child among them. At that rate, homosexuality would die out of the population in several generations. Obviously this hasn't happened. But about half of homosexuals are married, making them bisexuals with an average of 1.25 children each. That many children, on average, per bisexual is enough to keep the homosexual gene or genes alive in the population. Couldn't the homosexual gene or genes be kept in the gene pool that way? From a statistical point of view, no. Exclusive homosexuals and bisexuals, combined, still produce an average of only 0.9 children each, meaning that a homosexual gene or genes would still slowly, but inevitably, disappear from the gene pool.

• Homosexuality cannot be a genetic mutation. Although a genetically-based condition tends to stay in a family tree for generations, only very slowly and minimally changing its characteristics, a genetic mutation is one way it could appear suddenly. But for that to occur, many genes would have to mutate at the same time—an inconceivable scenario. Even five or six genes mutating at the same time is implausible, genetically speaking.

• About 90 percent of children in the West born with ambiguous genitalia choose to remain in their gender of upbringing when puberty reveals their true genetic gender and surgical interventions are offered. Often, this choice is made in the face of very contrary physical and hormonal characteristics. It argues for overwhelmingly strong environmental influences on the formation of gender orientation and behavior.

• The stages of psycho-social development toward adult heterosexuality are so clearly established and so obviously learned that heterosexuality is clearly not genetically mandated. Surveys of adult homosexuals show conspicuous deficits in several of these developmental

stages—arguing that homosexuality is also a learned behavior—a result of environmental conditioning rather
than genes.

   • A much higher homosexual incidence among those
who have been raised in large cities, rather than in rural
areas, argues that the environment is much more powerful than genes in the development of homosexuality.

   • Even Dean Hamer, one of the strongest advocates
of a genetic cause for homosexuality, has remarked that
he doesn't think a gene exists for sexual orientation. At
most, Hamer may have found a genetic effect for about
5 percent of the homosexual population. Gene linkage
studies are dubiously regarded by the scientific community.

   • Twin studies—make it quite clear that homosexuality is not determined, or all genetically identical co-
twins of homosexual men and women would also be homosexual. They also show that homosexuality is not
environmentally dictated. But it is dangerous to draw
any clearer conclusion from twin studies: (a) results are
far too contradictory (b) too many methodological re-
quirements are violated by homosexual populations under study with the result that "genetic" contributions to
homosexuality are significantly inflated.

   • There is so much scientific evidence of change
from homosexual orientation toward a heterosexual orientation that it is impossible to argue homosexuality is
genetically dictated.

Other Pointers to a Non-biological Homosexuality

   • Studies have shown no convincing relationship between homosexuality and exposure to pre-natal hormones.

   • Attempts to show the brain micro-structure of male
homosexuals is more like a woman's than a man's are
unconvincing when scientists have barely been able to
distinguish between male and female brains in adults.

Certainly, male and female brains appear identical at birth, and the only consistently replicable difference between male and female brains, from about age two or three, is their size. Most of the development of the human brain takes place after birth in response to stimuli, learning, and experience. In fact, the brain changes so much in response to learning and repeated human behaviors that any differences between homosexual and heterosexual brains, should they be discovered, could quite probably be thus accounted for.

• Our instincts, such as self-preservation, hunger, and reproduction, are among the most deeply embedded and strongest impulses we have, but these are able to be controlled. If we want to argue homosexuality is also a deeply ingrained instinct, it is also highly malleable and responsive to training.

• One final scientific tool, path analysis, which has been argued to show that there is no social or familial basis to homosexuality, but rather a biological one, in fact, did show social and familial links. Bell et al. did discover paths leading to homosexuality, but chose, for some reason, to say they were not significant, even though, in terms of the methodology, they were.

Geneticists, anthropologists, developmental psychologists, sociologists, endocrinologists, neuroanatomists, medical researchers into gender, and twin study researchers are in broad agreement about the role of genetics in homosexuality. Genes don't make you do it. There is no genetic determinism, and genetic influence at most is minor.

Genetic content of Homosexuality is Minor

Anyone who says homosexuality is dictated by genes doesn't know enough science. Those who say it's genetically influenced are correct, but only to about this degree:

If a girl becomes pregnant at age fifteen, we could
argue that she is genetically predisposed to. We
could say that in her culture, her genes gave her
the kind of face and figure that send male hormones into orbit and bring her under a level of
pressure that she is unable to resist. But that's
about the strength of the genetic influence. There
are a huge number of environmental factors that
could also have brought the pregnancy about—
from cancellation of the basketball game she was
going to watch with a girlfriend, permission to
borrow Dad's car, her boyfriend's company, the
movie they had just viewed together, and failure
to use a contraceptive, to big environmental factors like personal values systems, peer group pressure, and an emotionally distant father.

Is this consensus likely to change? Might some major
biological link be discovered which could change everything? After all, science moves fast.

Well, for most of these scientific disciplines, the findings have been clearly established from facts that will not
change significantly (the diversity of homosexual practices between and within cultures; the clearly established
stages of human development; the over-riding role of
upbringing in the ultimate gender choice of people with
ambiguous genitalia). But what of future studies of brain
micro-structure, or detailed analysis of genetic composi-
tion and function? Will they reveal links between brain
structure and human behaviors, or behaviors and genetic sequences? Of course they will. Probably papers
will continue to be published on the subject at the rate
of about half a dozen a year. We can safely conjecture
that even authors really concerned to prove such links
will almost always include the standard scientific caveats
that the influence is minor, and that the environment is
important. What we can reasonably conjecture about
future research is that it will enter new fields and come

up with new links, but none of them will be determinative.

The vast majority of human behaviors that have been measured by twin studies fall at or below the 50 percent mark. Bearing in mind that "heritability" means the level of genetic influence in the absence of contrary environmental influences, even behaviors of 50 percent heritability are not set in concrete (divorce, alcoholism, and criminality are subject to huge amounts of change by environmental intervention). Change will always ultimately lie in our hands, in the counteracting environmental influences we expose ourselves to.

So why do we have this idea that genes play such an important part in our behavior? There are a number of reasons.

1. The human genome project has focused a lot of attention and funding on genetic research and on behavioral genetics. When fascinating new fields are being explored, a disproportionate amount of significance can be attached to new discoveries, and there can be a loss of overall context.

2. The media are always looking for a "wow" factor that will sell newspapers and magazines and raise viewing ratings. Anything that hasn't been said or done before is of interest to the media. Put an exciting angle on it, create controversy if you can. Bring the media factor and competitive science together and accuracy can be a casualty while the words and pictures fly round the world in seconds to misinform millions. The fate of the 1992 United States National Research Council Report on violence and genes shows what can happen. What the report said was: violence arises from

> interactions among individuals', psychosocial development, neurological and hormonal differences, and social processes. . . . These studies suggest at most a weak role for genetic processes in influencing potentials for violent behavior. . . . If genetic

predispositions to violence are discovered they are
likely to involve many genes and substantial environmental interaction rather than any simple genetic marker.

What this important study was reported to say by the
New York Times was "Study cites role of biological and
genetic factors in violence."[1]

3. Gay activism, politics, fashion. Gay activism has
used and promoted any "evidence" that will bring powerful lobbies on its side in its campaign for acceptance of
the homosexual lifestyle. Homosexuality, as a genetic
inevitability, has probably won gays more sympathy than
any other single gay public relations initiative. Homosexuality now has important friends and supporters in
politics, the judiciary, the church, the health sector, arts,
Hollywood, the fashion industry, and the media. Genetic
homosexuality is an easy answer to a difficult question; it
has taken stigma away from homosexuality, and made it
possible for swathes of society to now say, "Gay is OK!"
Though it remains scientifically accurate to say homosexuality has trivial genetic content and correct to say
that homosexuals can become heterosexual, it is no longer
politically correct or fashionable to say it in many circles.

But it remains true—to say a behavior is "genetic" is
a logical fallacy—a simple lack of observation. Nothing is
forced on us by our biology. Even breathing isn't. The
fact is that nothing makes us do anything—neither our
genes nor our environment. No-one is trapped.

Are we, who are caught up in all manner of addictions, minor and major, sexual and spiritual going to
blame our biology, or our environment? Christians, at
least, are called to be part of the Fellowship of Continu-
ous Change, and part of the good news is that no one
needs to continue to be trapped in a behavior unless he
or she, in full possession of the facts, still agrees to be.
Science backs up the good news. You don't have to do
what your genes might predispose you to do, or what

your training in addictive behaviors begs you to do. You can re-train. You can be truly free.

We can change. Hard? Too hard? Well, we can be dead fish swept along by the current, or salmon who head into the rapids and waterfalls to reach the head of the river. Is all the heroic hard work worth it? Salmon are prepared to die in the attempt.

Jesus said, "Go into all the world and preach the good news." The good news includes the fact that change is possible. It's tremendous news, challenging news, divisive news. Jesus said he came to save the world, not condemn it, but he also said that the door leading to life is narrow and few find it. Change is a microcosm of the gospel. I am not trapped by my biology or my environment. I am able to get free—but it won't be easy. Does that mean some people will not finish the course, not make it out the other end? It seems so. People can be satisfied with their addiction. In other cases, our help, knowledge, and love may simply not be adequate.

We have a choice. We can give free reign to whatever genetic predisposition we might have toward a behavior, or we can, by grace, discipline, and divine help, counteract it.

DNA is a ladder of nitrogenous bases and sugars that makes proteins. But it is also a ladder of destiny, a Jacob's ladder, and it is our choice whether angels or demons walk up and down it. Do your genes make you do it? You choose.

I saw, struggling in a stagnant pool, a bee which had somehow fallen in. It flapped its wings futilely, and tried to dog-paddle, but made no progress. It seemed to be drowning. All around the bee were little creatures called water-fleas who hopped round, trouble-free on the surface of the water. They didn't seem interested in the bee at all.

I took the bee out of the pool using a dead leaf from a tree, and set it down nearby on the slate surround. The bee staggered off the leaf, drunkenly wandering in its new freedom, headed straight back to the pool and fell in again.

I lifted it out once more, and the bee staggered round rather aimlessly and seemed quite lost. I transferred it further away onto some grass. It tried to use its wings, but it looked to me as though they might be torn, and it might never fly again. It staggered from blade to blade, under some and over some in the three dimensional maze of the herbage. It even hopped from one blade to another, perhaps pathetically imagining it was flying.

Then—suddenly—after I had practically given up, it flew! It wove a surprisingly straight course through the airy dimensions, and was out of sight in seconds. I never saw it again.

This I know: that bee reached heights the water-fleas couldn't even dream of and so can you.

Notes

1. Nelkin, D., Lindee, M.S., *The DNA Mystique, The Gene As a Cultural Icon* (New York: W.H. Freeman, 1995).

For further information or help you might contact Exodus International, P.O. Box 77652, Seattle, WA 98177, (206) 784-7799, or exodus.base.org on the Web, alternatively NARTH, 16542 Ventura Boulevard, Suite 416, Encino, CA 91436, (181) 789-4440.

Index

fixity/fluidity of 7
gene linkages 139
male-female differences
    131
multiple genes, link to 18,
    19
selective breeding for 19
slow generational change
    of 19, 20, 27
theoretical constancy
    world-wide with time
    70, 98
Bestiality, cultural incidence
    99
Bisexuality 20, 25, 26, 36,
    37, 39-45, 100, 102,
    115, 116, 144, 157,
    186-188, 211
change of orientation,
    spontaneous 186-188
cultural variation 105-106
incidence 37, 39, 40
changes with age 41-43
male sex-hormones, ef-
    fects 113-115
marriage and 39, 40
sexual continua 20
Bowlby, J. 52
affection, effects of early
    deprivation 52
Boy raised as girl 90-92
reversion to biological
    gender 92
Brain anatomy
behavior, effects on struc-
    ture 126, 127
diagram 125
growth rate 126, 131

hypothalamus 126, 129
hypothalamus, size
    diagram 125
sexual orientation ef-
    fects 125
male-female differ-
    ences 125, 126, 129
rate of change of struc-
    tures 131
sexual orientation
    anterior commissure
    129, 130
    corpus callosum 130
    suprachiasmatic
    nucleus 129
sexual orientation, ef-
    fects 125-130, 213
    interaction 125-130

C

Castration, chemical
    sexual activity and 119
Castration, physical
    sexual activity and 120
Cells 28
complexity of 14-17
Child abuse 50, 51, 155
Childhood gender non-
    conformity 66-68, 121,
    155, 172-177
adrenogenital syn-
    drome 115
adult homosexuality,
    prediction of 68
fantasy in 118
Chromosomes, structure
    14

sexual orientation and
116
shared family environ-
ment 150-152
therapy, effects if condition mostly genetic 23
Erotic attraction
absence, for close rela-
tives 62
adrenogenital syndrome
88-90
age dependence 59, 60
androgen insensitivity
syndrome 117
cultural factors 62, 63
drugs, effects on, pla-
cebo effect 120, 121
exotic factors 62
independence of genes
or puberty 65
individualistic factors 63,
64
intersexes, upbringing
related 85
puberty and 59, 60
Estrogen, effects 59, 88,
118, 119
Ex-gay support groups 68,
69, 191, 194-195, 197,
200-204
Alcoholics Anonymous,
parallels 194, 195
program failures 194,
195

F

Fantasy 52

erotic 34, 40, 58-60, 70,
116-118, 188, 190
drugs, effects on 119
Female sex-hormones 113,
114, 118, 119
adult sexual orientation
interaction 118, 119
gender development
59
sexual activity and 118,
119
sexual orientation, ef-
fects on 113, 114, 118,
119
Frederick II, maternal
deprivation experiment
50, 51

G

Gender identity develop-
ment 51-59, 64-67, 69,
70, 87, 90-94, 115, 116
Gender, biological 86
development, in womb
113
Genetic diseases 21-24
incidence, compared to
homosexuality diagram
24
Genetics 7-10, 13-29, 40, 72
135-146, 160, 161, 214
aggression 22, 23, 139,
215, 216
Dutch study 22, 23
behavior incidence theo-
retically similar world-
wide 97

exclusive, diagram 38
influence of place of
upbringing 43, 44
path analysis 176-178
relationships, longevity
198
sex hormones
unbalanced (faulty hy-
pothesis) 118, 119
effects on 113-116
sexual abuse 68, 69
twin studies 149
heritability low 157-
158
vaginal inadequacy and
116
LeVay, S.
hypothalamus and
sexual orientation 126-
129
replication difficulties
129
results, diagram 128
Libido
drugs, effects on 119-
121
sex-hormones, effects on
119-121

M

Male sex-hormones 93,
113-121
adrenogenital syndrome
87-90
adult sexual orientation,
interaction with 118,
119

failure to produce, in
males 117
intersexes 59, 60
puberty 59
sexual activity and 59, 60,
119
sexual orientation, effects
on 113-119
Marriage 7, 25
arranged 62
intersexes 85
Masculinization
physiological 87-90, 93,
94, 113-116
homosexual incidence
unaffected 116
Maslow, A., Kinsey sex surveys 35
Masochism, development
63, 64
Masturbation, homosexual
development 178
Maternal stress
effects on child's sexual
orientation 117, 118
Media, genetics and 8,
138, 215, 216
Mendel, G. 18
Money, J. 87, 90, 91
identical twin, gender
change in 90, 91
intersex research 87-92,
115, 116
Monkeys, gender develop-
ment in 49, 50
Mothering 49-53, 56, 79-
81
affection, role of 50-52

We welcome comments from our readers. Feel free to write to us at the following address:

Editorial Department
Huntington House Publishers
P.O. Box 53788
Lafayette, LA 70505

or visit our website at:

www.huntingtonhousebooks.com

More Good Books from Huntington House Publishers

Hormonal Imbalance
The Madness and the Message
by Terry Dorian, Ph.D.

Safe, natural, and effective solutions to problems caused by hormonal imbalance. Discover how to end menopausal symptoms such as stress, confusion, hot flashes, night sweats, etc. Women from the beginning of puberty and throughout the post-menopausal years need this information in order to escape the horrors of hormonal imbalance.

Discover:

- *The deception of conventional Estrogen Replacement Therapy (ERT) and Hormone Replacement Therapy (HRT).*
- *How to end menopausal symptoms (hot flashes, night sweats, vaginal pain, bloating, and more) and reverse aging.*
- *Why you don't have to suffer from PMS.*
- *How to prevent and reverse osteoporosis, heart disease, and memory loss.*
- *Who the healthiest people in the world really are and why.*

ISBN 1-56384-156-8

Cloning of the American Mind
Eradicating Morality Through Education
by B. K. Eakman

Two-thirds of Americans don't care about honor and integrity in the White House. Why? What does Clinton's hair-splitting definitions have to do with the education establishment? Have we become a nation that can no longer judge between right and wrong?

"Parents who do not realize what a propaganda apparatus the public schools have become should read Cloning of the American Mind *by B. K. Eakman."*

—Thomas Sowell, *New York Post*
September 4, 1998

ISBN 1-56384-147-9

Government by Decree
From President to Dictator
Through Executive Orders
by James L. Hirsen, Ph.D.

Could Americans lose their constitutional rights and be forced to live under martial with the stroke of pen? Sound like fiction? Wrong! Right now, through the use of a tool call an executive order, the President of the United States has the power to institute broad, invasive measures that could directly impact the lives of average, everyday Americans. What might trigger the exercise of this type of awesome power? Any number of things could, but for certain, a crisis, real or manufactured, is the most frightening prospect.

ISBN 1-56384-166-5

Liberalism
Fatal Consequences
by W. A. Borst, Ph.D.

Liberalism indicted! *Liberalism: Fatal Consequences* will arm conservatives of all kinds (Christians, Orthodox Jews, patriots, concerned citizens) with the necessary historical and intellectual ammunition to fight the culture war on any front as it exposes the hypocrisy of liberalism.

"...an excellent critical examination of the issues that threaten to divide our nation."

—President Roche, Hillsdale College

ISBN 1-56384-153-3

The Coming Collision
Global Law vs. U.S. Liberties
by James L. Hirsen, Ph.D.

Are Americans' rights being abolished by International Bureaucrats? Global activists have wholeheartedly embraced environmental extremism, international governance, radical feminism, and New Age mysticism with the intention of spreading their philosophies worldwide by using the powerful weight of international law. Noted international and constitutional attorney James L. Hirsen says that a small group of international bureaucrats are devising and implementing a system of world governance that is beginning to adversely and irrevocably affect the lives of everyday Americans.

Paperback ISBN 1-56384-157-6
Hardcover ISBN 1-56384-163-0

One in a Million
An IRS Travesty
by Pat Shannan

A story for everyone who ever fantasized about getting back at the IRS!

"Pat Shannan uses the truth to create unbelievable fiction. I speak from the terror of brutal and life-threatening encounters during my 30-year battle against illegal and abusive government." —George Hansen, Seven term, U.S. Congressman

"This book provides an insight into the inner workings of an evil international shadow government that affects ours lives on a daily basis. Thank you Mr. Shannan for a wake-up call to all Americans. —Ted Gunderson, SAC (ret.) Los Angeles office of FBI

"...this novel will be the most suppressed book of the decade." —Gerald A. Carroll, Editor, *Media Bypass* magazine

ISBN 0-933451-42-3

Patriots
Surviving the Coming Collapse
by James Wesley, Rawles

Patriots, a fast-paced novel by Y2K expert James Wesley, Rawles is more than a novel — it's a survival manual. Could you survive a total collapse of civilization - a modern Dark Ages? Would you be prepared for the economic collapse, the looting, riots, panic, and complete breakdown of our infrastructure?

"More than just a novel, this book is filled with tips on how to survive what we all hope isn't coming to America." —Jefferson Adams, *The Idaho Observer*

ISBN 1-56384-155-X

ORDER THESE HUNTINGTON HOUSE BOOKS

- *Alien Intervention: Spiritual Mission of UFOs*—Paul Christopher
- *Anyone Can Homeschool*—Terry Dorian, PhD/Zan Peters Tyler
- *Basic Steps to Successful Homeschooling*—Vicki Brady
- *Beyond Political Correctness*—David Thibodaux, Ph.D.
- *Children No More*—Brenda Scott
- *Christian Revolution: Practical Answers to Welfare and Addiction*—Arthur Pratt
- *Cloning of the American Mind: Eradicating Morality Through Education*—B. K. Eakman
- *The Coming Collision: Global Law vs. U.S. Liberties*—James L. Hirsen, PhD
- *Communism, the Cold War, & the FBI Connection*—Herman O. Bly
- *The Cookbook: Health Begins in Him*—Terry Dorian, Ph.D.
- *Courting Votes in Alabama*—Winthrop E. Johnson
- *The Culture War in America*—Bob Rosio
- *Dark Cures: Have Doctors Lost Their Ethics*—Paul deParrie
- *The Deadly Deception*—Tom McKenney
- *The Demonic Roots of Globalism*—Gary Kah
- *The Disney Boycott*—Floyd McElveen
- *Do Angels Really Exist?*—Dr. David O. Dykes
- *The Eagles Claw: Christians and the IRS*—Steve Richardson
- *En Route to Global Occupation*—Gary Kah
- *From Earthquakes to Global Unity*—Paul McGuire
- *Gender Agenda: Redefining Equality*—Dale O'Leary
- *Getting Out: An Escape Manual for Abused Women*—Kathy Cawthon
- *Global Bondage*—Cliff Kincaid
- *Global Taxes*—Cliff Kincaid
- *The Gods Who Walk Among Us*—Thomas Horn/Donald Jones, PhD
- *Government by Decree*—James L. Hirsen, PhD
- *Health Begins in Him*—Terry Dorian, PhD
- *Hidden Dangers of the Rainbow*—Constance Cumbey
- *High on Adventure I, II, & III*—Stephen Arrington
- *Hormonal Imbalance*—Terry Dorian, PhD
- *How to Homeschool (Yes, You!)*—Julia Toto
- *It's Time to Start a Third Party*—Keith Snelson
- *A Jewish Conservative Looks at Pagan America*—Don Feder
- *Journey into Darkness*—Stephen Arrington
- *Liberalism: Fatal Consequences*—W. A. Borst, Ph.D.
- *Make Yourself Ready: Preparing to Meet the King*—Harland Miller
- *Millennium Time Bomb*—Charles H. Coppes
- *New World Order*—Bill Still
- *One Last Call*—Donnell Harris
- *One in a Million: An IRS Travesty*—Pat Shannan
- *Out of Control*—Brenda Scott
- *Outcome-Based Education*—Peg Luksik/Pamela Hoffecker
- *Patriots: Surviving the Coming Collapse*—James Wesley, Rawles
- *Prayer Without Ceasing... Breath Prayers*—Kathleen Lewis
- *The Slash Brokers*—Jeff S. Bargarnier
- *The Social Service Gestapo**—Janson Kauser
- *Spiritual Warfare: The Invisible Invasion*—Thomas R. Horn
- *What Would They Say? Founding Fathers on Current Issues*—Glen Gorton
- *Y2K:"...the event that could... paralyze a planet"*—Don Boys, PhD

*Available in Salt Series

Available at bookstores everywhere or order direct from:

Huntington House Publishers
P.O. Box 53788 • Lafayette, LA 70505

Call toll-free 1-800-749-4009